Picking in High Cotton

A Family's Remarkable Journey from Poverty to Prosperity

Shirley Robinson Sprinkles

Published by Wheatmark®
2030 East Speedway Boulevard, Suite 106
Tucson, Arizona 85719 USA
www.wheatmark.com

ISBN: 979-8-88747-132-7
LCCN: 2023915252

Bulk ordering discounts are available through Wheatmark, Inc. For more information, email orders@wheatmark.com or call 1-888-934-0888.

I am eternally grateful to have been ushered into this world by my parents, Copply Williams Robinson and Carl Henry Robinson. Their love and indefatigable patience formed the bedrock on which I've grown and built a life of which I'm proud. It is to them that I dedicate this book.

Contents

Foreword

Oh, what a tribute to the concepts of overcoming my friend has expressed in this wonderful story about her mother. What she's written resonates with me, as my maternal grandfather grew up on a cotton plantation as a child of sharecroppers. And I've picked cotton myself in one of the cotton fields in which Shirley Sprinkles's family toiled. But for me, it was just a way to earn a little spending change. For them, it was a hard way of life that compelled them to want to "become somebodies" someday.

I took in this story like pancakes absorbing drizzles of warm syrup and butter, finding it delicious how Shirley's mother lifted herself out of her life's hard conditions and went on to become someone of note. I could see how her determination for a better life affected my old classmate because she, too, is a doer, an achiever, a teacher of renown who went on to earn a PhD, attributes I first observed when we were in fourth grade at Dunbar Elementary and Junior High, the "colored school" we attended in Tucson. There we were encouraged to embrace our Blackness and prove to ourselves and the world that we deserved the unadulterated rights white people enjoyed. Our motto was "Be the Best."

And my dear friend has, like her mother, lived the spirit of such a creed and has, in a glorious fashion, shed a light in this wonderful read as to what that's all about. She's still "picking in high cotton," still doing well, because in a world that demands much of us, we must pick until we reach the end of our row.

I'd dare say that anyone reading the following pages will feel in themselves a little boost in their get-up-and-go.

Written endearingly with everlasting respect,
Ernie McCray

Introduction

A nationwide emigration took place in the United States between the years 1931 and 1958. It was the migration of Black people from the South to other places—the North, East, and West—anyplace to escape from suffocating, intractable Jim Crow oppression. The trek required leaving behind family, friends, familiar places, and traditions. The hope of finding opportunity and economic advancement and living more dignified lives seemed well worth the trade-off.

The greatest challenge was finding work to sustain life in these new, strange places. Picking cotton was work that these migrant Black people were familiar with; qualifications were minimal—two legs, two hands, a set of reasonably good eyes, a strong back, and the ability to withstand long hours in blistering heat. They would pull long sacks packed with fluffy balls of white cotton. Highly qualified, thousands of Blacks set out to find employment in myriad cotton fields that were strung out across the Southwest, all the way to the California border and beyond.

It is in just such a field, located in a small eastern Arizona town, Safford, that this story begins. It is a typical, although seldom told, story about tight-knit seasonal cotton pickers who share a complex subculture in which the convergence of benevolence, derelictions, faith, and friendships takes place. Pain, pleasure, camaraderie, and fun characterize the group's daily experiences as they toil to make living wages.

Some people are ashamed that they picked cotton—too close to dreadful images of slave-driven labor, I suppose. For others, like me, it evokes proud memories of multiple cotton-field "mini societies" replete with individuals working daily side-by-side under an unrelenting hot sun, sharing unanimity of purposeful goals: survival, resiliency, dignity. In the cotton patch, there was no differentiation of class or status—we were all equally poor, striving to eke out a living, working at what was available to us. What I fondly and positively remember are various scenarios in which our diverse versions of humanity were on display.

Most of all, my recollections focus on those times when a mysterious wave of pure joy swirled in the air above the heads of us cotton pickers, seemingly shading us temporarily, like a huge, leafy willow tree, not just from a merciless sun but also from the oppression of physical and emotional pain; times when there was the spontaneous singing of a familiar hymn or gospel song; and those fun times when a familiar blues tune that everyone knew the words to floated up and was carried across dozens of cotton rows. Oh, what a joyous time that could

become! Improvised harmonizing and soloing often characterized these love-laced sessions—one song leading to another
and another, with a lot of verbal confirmation floating across
multiple rows of bent backs that often popped up, moved,
grooved, and swayed to different melodies. Work became
less agonizing as the spirit glided through the air, converting
drudgery of toil to pure joy.

I never want to forget that segment of my long life. I'm
confident that it shaped my earliest awareness of Black culture
and community and my place in it. It was that awareness that
imprinted the constructs of character, resilience, determination, hope, tenacity, and aspiration on my soul—attributes that
define me to this very day.

I'm betting that others like me, no matter their skin color,
who worked in cotton fields picking the "white gold" that built
the wealth of this country understand the depth and richness
of those unique cotton patch experiences.

This is a story about the indomitable spirit of a woman
whose determination, courage, tenacity, and resilience led her
whole family out of poverty and onto a path of high success.
I am proud to say that she was my mother, my guiding light
for all the years that she was part of my life. Her story proves
that one need not wither and die under the burdens of racial,
economic, marital, or any other obstructive social construct.
She did not succumb to negativity; instead, she selected and

followed trails that led to opportunity—opportunity to use her innate gifts of personality as well as mental and emotional strengths to scale walls of obstacles that threatened her success.

There's something within me that holdeth the reins;
Something within me that banishes pain;
Something within me—I cannot explain;
All that I know is there's something, something, within!
(Negro spiritual)

It is my hope that readers will find encouragement in this story with its many interwoven complexities of diverse relationships. Writing it laid bare many undiscovered parts of my own person as Copply's daughter, as someone's wife, and as mother to a thriving brood of offspring.

"Dare to struggle, dare to win" is a slogan that I think befits and summarizes both of our lives. I'm glad we were privileged to do it together.

When asked, "What's next?" I proudly respond, "I'm just gonna keep pickin' till I get to the end of my row."

PART

1

"The important thing is this: to be able at any moment to sacrifice what we are for what we could become."
(Charles Dubois)

Cotton-Field *Life*

Inside a small two-room housing unit where cotton pickers live rent-free, Copply lifts Shirley, a sleeping toddler, off the bed and onto her shoulder.

"Come on, sleepyhead, time to go!" She kisses her forehead lightly.

She grabs the blanket and wraps it snugly around the child before starting out for the home of the neighbor lady who cares for Shirley while her parents work in the cotton fields. She crosses the dirt and gravel cul-de-sac that separates the apartments of Black and Mexican workers.

"Good mornin', Miss Gonzales. Here's our little angel."

She pries the sleeping child off her shoulder and transfers her to the waiting arms of Mrs. Gonzales, who smiles broadly, takes the child into her arms, and responds, "Tenga buen día, señora."

"Gracious."

This is the only Spanish word that Copply attempts. Although it isn't exactly *gracias,* Mrs. Gonzales understands and waves goodbye before closing her door. She will care for Shirley and her own five young children today, as she does every day while her husband is also away picking cotton.

As Copply crosses the road back to her home, she can't help thinking how grateful she is for Mrs. Gonzales. Without her, life would be much harder.

Br-r-r-i-n-g! Carl jerks up from his sleeping position, slaps the clock to stop the alarm, and falls back on the pillow. He slowly sits up, yawns, and wipes his eyes while pushing the window shade aside to peer outside. It's still dark. He hears Copply rattling pots in the kitchenette of their one-room living quarters. He breathes in a pungent smell of coffee. He rushes to the water closet to pee before hastily pulling on his work trousers and boots. He looks up toward Copply.

"Where the kids?" Carl stares sleepily at the empty twin bed.

"Daddy picked Junior up last night, and Mrs. Gonzales is gonna keep Shirley today." Copply swats at a small cockroach as she answers.

Carl reaches for the long-sleeved shirt to slip over his sleeveless undershirt. Next, he grabs the all-important water canteen and a wide-brimmed straw hat. He gently brushes Copply out of his way at the sink.

"Make haste, Cope—we don't want to miss the truck."

Copply puts one hand on her left hip, stands back on the other leg, and cocks her head to look Carl squarely in the eyes.

"You know, Carl, you really should spend more time with these kids. They don't hardly know you. They hardly ever see you. They miss you. Shirley is always asking for you. 'Papi? Papi?' Where do you go every day after work? I don't see much of you either."

Carl does not respond to her question. She searches his face. He is mute, ignoring her—again. Angry at his behavior, she plops down in a chair, reaches for the latest copy of the *Chicago Defender* newspaper, and begins noisily turning pages. He snatches the newspaper out of Copply's hands.

"Put that damn newspaper down! All you do is read. We don't have time for that!"

Copply, a tall, slender, light-skinned woman, rolls her eyes at Carl and replaces the newspaper on a stack of old newspapers on the floor. Then she steps up her pace, yanking on a large piece of cloth that she wraps around her head, and ties it in a knot at the nape of her neck. She pulls on a pair of Carl's old pants and a long-sleeved shirt. Her work boots are high and wide. She grabs a big sun bonnet, a sack of sandwiches from the ice box, and a lightweight thermos bottle as she sprints out the slamming door.

The couple arrives at the corner of their residential block just in time to be the last boarders of a large flatbed truck with side rails. It will transport the dozen or so cotton pickers to the vast fields that line the highway on both sides as far as the eye can see. They will start picking new rows near where they left off yesterday—each row, burgeoning with white fluffy cotton pushing out from sticky burrs, stretches about three quarters of a mile.

Pickers start just as the sun comes up, pick until noon, take a brief lunch break, and resume picking until the sun's last rays. Cotton pickers are not paid by the hour—they earn their pay by pounds picked in a day. A weigh station and pay master determine their value—nothing more, nothing less.

Carl reaches for her hand and helps Copply off the truck.

"Come on, Copply. We hafta get five hundred pounds today. Gotta buy groceries and pay on the car on Saturday. Your mama and daddy need a little help too. And don't forget our church tithes. You oughta pick with Sister Bessie today; she won't waste time flapping her lips. Keep away from that Dorothy Sue gal; she'll slow you down with her gossip and wild stories—you don't have time for that!"

"I wish you wouldn't boss me around so much! I'm a grown woman, not your child. I'll pick with whoever I want—just like you do. I don't say nothing about that lying Bunkie Lee or whorish James Willie that you love to pick with. Y'all stop working once every hour to hoorah and laugh—laugh so loud they can hear you all the way in town! So, mind your own business and leave mine alone!"

Copply snatches her cotton sack and lunch bag from the truck and saunters off haughtily. Carl adjusts his hat forward over his eyes and scratches his head as if perplexed by Copply's words. No time to figure it out right now. She'll be all right by sundown.

The pickers choose their rows and fan out across the field to begin working. There are diverse ways of securing the long cotton sacks: Some are tied around waists within easy reach of the hips while bent over. Others are secured with a wide cloth cross-shoulder band that raises the mouth of the sack higher to the armpit. Some sacks are longer than others, but all will be stuffed to capacity more than once today.

Copply shades her eyes with her hand as she peers upward at a warm bright sun that is already positioning itself to rise high and hot in a cloudless sky. She speaks to Sister Bessie as she adjusts her shoulder strap.

"O-o-o-e-e-e! That's a mean sun coming up. It's gonna be a hot one! Glad I brought my new sun bonnet. How you like it?"

Bessie turns, looks all around Copply's head, and nods her approval.

The women separate themselves from the men—they have a lot to discuss, private talk for their ears only. They will pick up where they left off yesterday, sharing juicy gossip, recipes, and sage advice. Topics will range from men to church life to children—plenty to pass the time and dispel fatigue.

As the work gets started, Bessie turns toward Copply. "How are those young'uns of yours? Haven't heard you say anything about them lately. How're they adjustin' to Arizona? Last we talked, you were a little worried about the baby. Is she all right?"

"Junior is doing fine. He spends a lot of time with Mother Daisy and with Daddy when he's home. That's good for him since Carl Henry is gone a lot. Shirley is doing better now since we found out what was wrong with her."

"What was the problem?" Bessie looks puzzled. "You said she acts funny—always crying and irritable."

"Yes, ma'am. She was a mess when we had her at home on weekends. She jabbered all day long, but we couldn't understand a word of what she was saying. Then she'd fall out on the floor if she pointed to something and we didn't give it to her. So, you know that called for a butt spanking. We're not tryin' to raise no spoiled child! Last week, we finally found out the problem."

Betty, Dorothy, and Christine stop picking and lean in to hear the rest of the discussion.

"What was it?" they all ask in concert.

"Well, Joe Brown stopped by the house for a visit just when Shirley was going into one of her fits. She kept yelling something like *agua, agua*. Just as I was about to yank her off the floor, Joe asked me why she couldn't have some water since it was hot as hell. He grabbed a cup and poured some water into it and handed to her. She gulped the water down and reached out for more. After that, she was quiet and went off to play with her doll. I was amazed. I asked Joe how he knew what to do."

"Yeah, *agua* means *water* in Spanish," Betty Jo piously interjects.

"Well, that was news to me. Joe said he's heard that child speaking Spanish for a long time. He laughed so hard when he saw the expression on Carl's face—you could have bought him for a dime! Here we thought the child was handicapped. She's old enough to talk plainly, but it sounded like gibberish to us. And to think, we've been spanking her for speaking the only language she knows. I have to pray hard and ask God to forgive me. I just didn't know."

"Well, I declare!" Sister Bessie bellows.

The women laugh loudly, stopping to hold their sides. A couple of them make mocking sounds: "Agua! Agua!" More laughter as they move along.

Copply, slightly chagrined by the mocking, looks back down the field they've covered briefly. She shades her eyes with her bonnet and speaks about another subject.

"Pearl didn't make it today. Wonder what happened."

"I think she's got TB," Bessie says in a concerned voice. "Didn't you notice how she was coughin' last week? I was scared to get too close to her. She looked bad, and I believe she was spittin' up blood. I'm glad she stayed home."

"Sho' 'nuff?" Copply stops dead still. "That's terrible. I need to go see about my friend. No tellin' what condition her and them kids are in. I'll take some chicken and greens if she don't show up tomorrow. I hope they're all right."

"Well," says Dorothy Sue, "I don't aim to spread gossip, but I heard her no-good husband ain't been home in two weeks. He's s'posed to be goin' with a woman from Tucson that keeps him occupied. Men can be so low down!"

"Well, if you ask me," says Christine, "he's too fine for Pearlie Mae anyhow. O-o-o-w-e-e! That man sho' is a long, cool drink o' water! He is *so* fine!" The women laugh softly. "Pearlie betta watch out—I just might get my hands on him!"

Betty Jo doesn't find Christine's comments funny.

"I betta never catch my ol' man with another woman. I got sumthin' for both of 'em!" She raises two clenched fists in the air.

The women release a loud cackling sound of laughter that affirms Betty's words.

"I *know* that's right!"

"Me, too, Betty!"

Their chatter, ranging from cooking to children, proceeds as they pick the cotton, pausing from time to time to glance across the field to see where the men are.

Footsteps are heard as Pearlie Mae runs to catch up to the ladies, her empty sack under her arm. She pants heavily as she arrives. Her face is badly bruised and scratched. One eye is swollen and nearly closed. Her busted lip still seeps a trickle of blood. She collapses, out of breath, on the ground, where the women halt work, picking her up to attend to her.

"Oh my God Almighty, child! What happened to you?" Copply shouts with alarm.

Copply and Sister Bessie kneel to hold Pearlie Mae up and take a closer look at her wounds. Only tearful sobbing comes from Pearlie. She is too distraught to speak.

"Cain't y'all see that man done beat the shit out of her?" Dorothy Sue crosses her arms in an angry gesture as she spouts out her diagnosis.

"A damn shame! He oughta go to jail." Betty Jo waves her arms, shouting angrily.

"All I did was ask him where he'd been for two days," Pearlie stammers between halting sobs. "I asked him nicely. He just started swinging at me with his fists like he was fightin' a man. I begged him to stop. The kids was watching. They was so scared!" More wails.

All the women huddle protectively around Pearlie Mae in a group hug. After a short time, Pearlie rises to her feet, adjusts her cotton sack, finds a row, and starts picking. Each of the women shares a pile of cotton from their sacks with Pearlie to catch her up. The work commences anew.

"You just pray and ask the Lord to help you, Pearlie. He'll hear and answer your prayers," Bessie calmly advises. She begins singing an old Negro spiritual, "He Will Carry You Through."

The other women join in with the harmony. Then, as if inspired by their own voices, they start another spiritual song, harmonizing into vocal parts as if singing in a choir: "Take Your Burdens to the Lord."

Pearlie, feeling somewhat better, turns her face away from the others, looks toward the sky, and sings quietly, as if to herself. "I Must Tell Jesus."

Copply shades her eyes with her hands, this time to look for Carl Henry across the field where the men are picking. When she spots him, she waves. He waves back.

"Betty Jo, I see you holding your belly." Copply turns her head toward Betty, who has suddenly halted her picking. "Now, don't you have that baby right out here in this cotton patch!"

Betty manages a painful smile, lowers her head, and begins picking again. She doesn't want that to happen either.

Carl Henry, dark and handsome with slicked-back, wavy hair, and the group of men he's picking with pause from work to drink water from their canteens. Carl shakes his head vigorously.

"It's hotter than hell out here today. I don't know if I can make it to quittin' time. There has got to be a better way to make a livin'. I'm not cut out for this. Texas wasn't this hot!"

He pulls a rag from his hip pocket and wipes his wet face. All of the men take turns looking up at the cloudless blue sky.

"Looks like we could at least get a breeze," complains Bunkie Lee. Bunkie adjusts the strap of his sack to relieve tension. "I'll be glad when we get to the end of these rows. I'm sure hungry. That bologna and cheese sandwich is sho' gon' taste good. It's callin' me. I hope they haven't jacked up the price. I need enough to buy some red soda water to cool my burnin' throat. Come on, boys, let's get movin'. We cain't make no money back here."

"We cain't make no money out here in this cotton patch no how," Carl laments. "I hate this back-breaking, low-life-ass work. I don't have a whole lot of book learnin', but that don' keep me from wantin' to be *somebody* in life. I want to be somebody, man—you understand? Be *somebody*! I gotta get up out of here—soon and very soon!"

"Wait . . . I want to hear that song ol' Slick here promised to play on his mouth harp before we start up again," says James Willie, a.k.a. Skillet. "I need a little inspiration for my perspiration."

He chuckles, straightens his back, crosses his arms, smirks, and turns his cocked head in the direction of where Slick is standing, preparing to move on. The men laugh and coax Slick to hurry up and play something.

Slick fumbles for his harmonica, which is buried deep in his khaki pants pocket. When he finds it, he jokingly tells the men he's going to collect a fee when they get paid. He commences to play and sing, "I Got a Woman."

The song is rhythmic. The harmonica plays a sweet and whiny accompaniment, causing the men to bob and sway. They chime in, singing the words and taunting Slick to say her name. He teases a quick nod of his head in the direction of where the women are picking.

Skillet casts a furtive glance across the field. "You talkin' 'bout Christine?" He laughs a chortling, deep-throated, derisive laugh. "Let me tell you something, shorty. You're 'bout to catch a tiger by the tail. If you don't know what you're doing, you sho' betta ask somebody 'cause you gon' be *pickin' in high cotton!*"

Just then, Christine stops and stretches her arms to the sky, revealing her long, shapely body. Carl and Bunkie Lee release a loud, flirtatious whistle in concert. Now they start up picking again, eyeing the distance ahead to where they can spot the weigh scales and cotton wagon that will take their day's work to the cotton gin.

Bunkie, inspired by the conversation sparked by Slick's song, starts to sing his version of a song that addresses the topic: "I'm Gonna Move to the Outskirts of Town."

Jack, the preacher, breaks away from the group and starts picking alone. He is an older man and doesn't participate in such worldly male banter anymore. He's contemplating the words he will say in his sermon on Sunday morning when these same people will become his parishioners, the biblical stories he will tell for the umpteenth time about the woman at the well, David and Goliath, Paul and Silas, the three boys in the fiery furnace, and Daniel in the lions' den. He begins practicing how he wants to sound—alternating the cadence of his loud and soft words with a singsong whine that takes him from one story to the next. The theme of the sermon will be "Jesus saves—He can save *you!*"

"I'm just a *nobody* tryin' to tell *everybody* about a man named Jesus who can save sinners, men and women, boys and girls—everybody!" In his characteristic "whoop" style of preaching.

Jack imagines his skillful moves across the small stage (pulpit) on which his hand-hewn wooden podium stands. He repeats the chant-like phrase. When he hears a faint *hallelu-jah* shouted from across the field, he realizes that his "practice" session has carried over the hot air waves to the ears of Sister Bessie. Now she's happy and shouting like she does in church. Cotton is flying everywhere around her, but she is oblivious to it as she fervently jumps up and down in her familiar religious trance, flinging her arms about, giving in to a spirit that has overcome her. Her companions rush to calm her—frantically fanning her with their straw hats and rags used for wiping away sweat.

The men, hearing the ruckus coming from across the field, pause to observe what's happening. Seeing the familiar sight—Sister Bessie expressing herself—they shake their heads and return to their work.

"If Rev thinks he's gonna save *me*, he sho' better pull on some high boots 'cause he sho' will be pickin' in HIGH cotton!"

This remark by Bunkie Lee strikes the other men in the group as very funny. They let out the loudest laugh of the day and repeat the phrase in concert as they start to move on: "Pickin' in high cotton!"

"Walk with Me, Lord, Walk with Me," Bessie's melodic voice belts out the familiar inspirational church song.

Jack counters with a different gospel song: "Goin' up Yonder."

Now the entire field of cotton pickers starts to sing this song—they've caught the spirit.

Copply breaks away from the group of women and begins to pick up a fast pace. She can't hang back with them any longer; she has a four-hundred-pound goal to make. She's picking cotton on both sides of her—two rows at a time. Her head is down now. She adjusts the heavy cotton sack on her square shoulders and moves rapidly ahead. Carl looks up, noticing her motion across the field.

"Look at her!" Carl leans over to hunch Bunkie Lee's shoulder. "She's almost to the end of her row already. That girl is a natural-born hustler. Won't be long before we can buy that new car!"

Bunkie murmurs under his breath, "She's the one who's gonna be somebody!"

Lunch time brings a brief spell of relief—a time to rest; smoke cigarettes; eat cold-cut sandwiches made of bologna, salami, and cheese; and drink the ice-cold strawberry, orange, and cola sodas that are sold on the vending truck. There's also a keg of cold water on the side of the truck and a dipper that they share for drinking. Just in time, a cloud moves over the spot, providing welcome shade from the blistering sun. There are no toilets. People fan out across the fields to find secluded spots to squat and relieve themselves on the ground. It's hard to resist the temptation to stretch out somewhere and take a nice nap.

Everyone, especially Carl, looks forward to closing out this hot, dry day. He, Slick, Bunkie, and Skillet find a shady spot, clear a section of flat ground with their hands, and start a crap game with a pair of dice.

"Come on, seven," Carl calls out to the dice as he shakes them, then tosses them on the ground. "Baby needs a new pair o' shoes!"

Bunkie puts out the cigarette he's been smoking and securely places a new one behind his right ear before he takes the dice for his turn.

The game is short but fun. It's soon time to get back to work.

"Y'all be careful out there," Bunkie calls out as he gathers up his freshly emptied sack. "I saw one of them rattlesnakes back there coiled up under a cotton stalk. Keep your eyes peeled!"

No sooner has he said that than Copply stops dead still in her new row. First, she hears the clear sound of a rattle. Then she sees a long brown snake slowly slither across her path, just ten feet ahead. She is frozen. She waits until he's out of sight before proceeding—with great caution.

As the sun begins to set, the men and women have picked the equivalent of about four miles of cotton rows. They line up at the pay master's station to turn in their tickets in exchange for cash. Copply carefully examines her dollar bills to be certain that all of the money she's owed is there. She's quick with math; it was her best subject in the small all-Black schools she attended back in Texas.

When she's satisfied with the twenty dollars she has earned, she tucks the bills into her bosom and walks wearily toward the truck that will take her home—home to children, cooking, and cleaning; home to a disgruntled husband who can't wait to eat, bathe, and get out into the streets, where he will spend most of the night again. But first, she will go by Pearlie's house to see how her best friend is feeling. She has had a hard day. Maybe she can use some help.

Pearlie Mae returns home to a different situation. She can't afford a babysitter for her three children, so the oldest child, Mary Beth, age seven, takes care of her siblings, ages four and two, until her mother returns home from the fields. The house is in total disarray; dirty clothes, soiled diapers, and remnants of jelly sandwiches are strewn everywhere. Pearlie is too tired and sore from the beating to scold the children. She hugs them stiffly and plops down on a dirty cushioned armchair to rest before beginning the tasks of straightening the house, washing clothes and diapers in a tin tub, scrubbing them clean on a rub board, hanging them outside on a clothesline, and preparing some sort of meal for the children.

There's no one to help her. Her husband has left the children alone and gone back to his other life. Surveying her dismal surroundings saddens Pearlie to the point of tears, but she stifles them. The kids must not see the depth of her despondence—no sense scaring them again. She coughs deeply—very deeply.

Knock, knock. Pearlie sits up and pulls back the tattered curtain to see Copply at her front door. Hastily, she starts to pick up items on the floor, shoving some of them under the unmade bed. She's ashamed for her friend to see these squalid conditions. Copply's persistent hard knocks cannot be ignored. Pearlie opens the door and invites Copply in.

"Girl, you didn't tell me you were comin' over here after work so soon."

"Well, I really hadn't planned to, but I couldn't help worrying about you. How are you feeling? What can I do to help you? It was a long, hot day out there—and after what you've been through . . ."

Pearlie starts to tear up but holds back. Struggling to regain her composure, she walks toward the kitchen and begins running water to wash a sink full of dirty dishes. Copply follows her, searches until she finds a broom, and starts sweeping up trash, diapers, food remnants, and broken toys. She silently sorts and tosses the debris. Next, she makes up the bed and dusts the few pieces of furniture. As Pearlie works in the kitchen, Copply calls Mary Beth to come to her, where she seats her on a kitchen chair and combs her disheveled hair into three neat plaits. The women say very little while they work, as if words would get in their way. Pearlie coughs a lot.

When order is restored, Copply looks in the bathroom cabinet for aspirins. She locates a small tin container of them, directs Pearlie to sit down and rest, gives her a glass of water, watches her swallow the pills, and hugs her. It's past time for her to pick up Shirley from Mrs. Gonzales. She turns to leave, promising to see her friend in the fields tomorrow.

Pearlie exhales a long sigh of relief, thanks Copply again and again, then, hearing the door close, leans back in the chair and whispers a prayer of gratitude for a friend like Copply. She doesn't know when things will change for her. She wishes she were as strong as her dear friend. For now, she will continue to pray.

Trouble Brews

Copply goes to Mrs. Gonzales's home to pick up Shirley.

"Ella no está aquí." Gesturing with her hands to help her explain to Copply that Shirley isn't there, Mrs. Gonzales adds, "El papá la recogió." Again, her hand gestures indicate that Carl took the child away.

"Where?"

Mrs. Gonzales shrugs her shoulders, indicating that she doesn't know. This has never happened before. This is very strange and very disturbing. Copply begins a door-to-door search of the neighbors on her side of the cul-de-sac, asking everyone if they witnessed Carl picking up their daughter. Everyone says no. Perhaps he took her to the grand-parents' house.

She rushes to the apartment where Sister Bessie lives alone. Bessie has barely arrived home before she hears a frantic knock at her door. She opens it to find Copply, who nervously blurts out something about Shirley missing.

"Sister Bessie, I need your help. Carl Henry took Shirley

from Mrs. Gonzales early this afternoon, and I don't know where she is. I have to find her. Can you take me to my father's house? Maybe they're over there."

"Lord have mercy, Jesus! Just give me a minute to change clothes. We'll go find that baby!"

Shortly, when Bessie is changed into street clothes, the two women get into the car and drive off. Copply directs Bessie to Roger and Daisy's house, where they find Daisy—"Big Mama" to the kids—sitting in her rocker on the front porch. When she sees them drive up, she reaches for her spit can and unloads a fresh dip of snuff. She stands to greet the ladies. Copply frantically asks her if she has seen Carl and Shirley. Daisy shakes her head, *no*. She adds that Junior is with Roger—"Papa" to the kids—at the grocery store.

"Bring her over here when you find her. I'm planning to make her favorite banana pudding tonight. She'll love that!"

Copply laughs a faint laugh. Nothing is funny right now. Where is her child?

The two women get back into the car.

"Sister Bessie, will you please take me into town? I'll bet that fool has her in that juke-joint café where those soldiers hang out. I'm pretty sure he didn't take her to church! I have to find her."

"You reckon he'd do something that stupid?"

Copply and Sister Bessie drive to the café-saloon in town and rush in the door. The place wreaks with the odor of liquor.

There at the bar sits Carl Henry, surrounded by a group of men, some of them soldiers, who are drinking and laughing loudly at what is taking place. Little Shirley sits on the bar counter, feet dangling in front of her father, combing out the long bangs of his hair, which are usually slicked back with stiff hair grease. Someone has given her a pocket-size comb, and she is playing "beauty shop" with her father's hair like she does with her doll. He accommodates her by holding his head down low enough for her to reach. She is having fun, and the onlookers are amused. They join in the fun, shouting instructions to the little beautician.

"Give him a pompadour!"

"How about some sideburns?"

"I think he wants a part in the middle."

Carl loves this daughter of his and enjoys the attention she playfully gives him in the midst of his intoxicated friends.

"Y'all need another round of beer. Set 'em up, bartender." He pulls out a wad of bills and tosses them onto the bar. He stops laughing when he sees Copply and Sister Bessie come in the door. "Copply! What are *you* doing here?"

"No, what are *you* doing here? And with this child! You don' lost your mind! Hand her here. I'm taking her home! You can stay if you want but not with my child!"

Copply delivers a hard slap to the right jaw of Carl's face. She grabs Shirley off the counter and carries her in her arms toward the door. Shirley is screaming for her father. "Papi! Papi!"

Bessie shoots a harsh, scolding look at everyone present in the cantina as she wags her finger at them. "I'm gonna pray for all y'all sinners!"

She stomps defiantly out the door to join Copply and the child.

When they arrive home, Copply says, "Thank you, Sister Bessie. You have been a dear friend. I'll always remember your kindness. Keep praying for me."

They hug twice. Shirley darts out of the car and into the house, hoping to find Carl Jr. Copply notices the moving window shades of her neighbors and coworkers as she drags herself wearily into the house to deal with the children and the chores awaiting her in her own household. She feels drained from all the emotion she has spent today—not the least of which is her dismay over this last episode with Carl. Now she sees with her own eyes *why* they can't get ahead. They are married, but they're just not on the same page.

The Last *Straw*

Bang! Bang! Bang! "Open this do'!"

It's Carl Henry returning home at 4:00 a.m. Copply is not asleep, but she pretends not to hear him and doesn't get up to unlock the door.

After several more attempts to get into the house, Carl returns to his car and curls up in the back seat. He's intoxicated. He quickly dozes off to sleep. Copply quietly opens the door and steps out to the car. Finding the car door ajar, she opens it and discovers a woman's brassiere on the front seat. It's not hers.

Angrily, she jerks the bra off the seat and carries it into the house. She reaches for the box of matches on top of the stove, takes out one, strikes it and is ready to set the brassiere on fire. Holding it by one end, away from her, she hurries back outside but decides to wait. She has a better idea. She must not act too rashly. The right time will come, just not right now. She suspects it belongs to that hussy, Christine, who she saw in the cantina drinking and hanging out with all the good-timers.

She'll wait to burn it. For now, she hides it under the bed. She wakes Carl up. They argue. He leaves again.

For Copply, this is the last straw—her mind is made up. She will not put up with Carl's drinking, gambling, and womanizing anymore. She will pack her and the kids' few belongings in the old canvas suitcase and hide it under the bed. Then she will go to work as usual, say goodbye to Pearlie, her most trusted secret-bearer in the field, tell Mother and Daddy that she's leaving, and head out of town when Carl goes to sleep. This is a plan long in the making, but now she has the courage to execute it. She's determined to make a new start—somewhere.

The children will miss their home—especially their grandparents and probably their father too, but change is necessary.

When the truck comes the next day, Carl does not get on it. He's sleeping off a drunken hangover. Copply goes to the field without him. When the women get to their spot, she calls Pearlie aside to tell her of her plans.

"I can't tell you just where I'm going 'cause I really am not sure right now just which direction I'll take—east or west. All I know, Pearl, is that I've reached the end of my row here. I'm done with Carl Henry's foolishness. The kids and I will start over."

Tears well up in her eyes. Pearlie sobs. The two tearful friends hug tightly.

"I'm gonna miss y'all so much. Pray for me."

Copply then admonishes her friend to take care of herself until they meet again. The two friends hug once more before Copply turns and walks with strong, deliberate steps in the opposite direction, head up high, sackless.

When Roger and Daisy come to deliver Carl Jr. home that evening, Copply tearfully tells them her plans. Her parents are sad but supportive. They know there's been trouble in the marriage.

"Now, Hunk," Roger says after clearing the lump in his throat. "Hunk" is his nickname for Copply. "Don't you go too far away. I want to be able to reach you if you need me."

Copply hugs him tightly, sobbing. Daisy joins in and hugs her tightly, wiping tears, but doesn't speak. She has been lonely here in Safford. The children were her only source of joy. She longs to return to Texas to reunite with her five children from a previous marriage. If Roger follows Copply again, she will not go with him.

Roger tells the children: "Now y'all be good. Don't make me have to come after you with my switch!"

The children nod their heads up and down vigorously.

Copply waits for Carl to get home with the car and fall asleep. She quietly packs the suitcases into the trunk. Before she gathers up the children, she has just one more important thing to do: she pulls that damned brassiere out from under the bed, gets the matches from the kitchen, steps outside, and sets the bra on fire. She wants to see it smoldering as she drives away—sweet revenge!

Next, she reaches for her hidden stash of money that is also under the bed in a coffee can. She counts out one hundred dollars and places it in her bosom—in her own bra—next to a slip of paper that is a rent receipt for what she hopes will soon be a place to stay for herself and the children.

She wraps sleeping Shirley in a blanket and places her snugly on the back seat. Junior will ride next to her in the front seat. She puts the gear in neutral and coasts a good distance backwards before starting the engine. When it's safe, she starts the motor, pulls down the first gear and drives slowly over the short, narrow bridge that crosses over the shallow irrigation ditch that runs behind the workers' apartments. Here, there is a road that leads out of the housing compound and onto the highway. Lights are starting to come on in the houses as she drives away. There's no turning back.

"Mama, where we going?" Carl Jr. inquires sleepily.

"Shh!" Copply places a finger to her lips in a gesture that tells him to be silent.

Now she turns on the headlights and steps on the gas. The car picks up speed as it heads west toward the next town. There's an arrow pointing west on the first sign she sees. It says "TUCSON."

When Carl wakes up, things are very different. Neither Copply nor the kids are there. No coffee is brewing in the kitchen. He is alone. He rises and opens the door to look outside. The car is gone. There on the steps is the charred remnant of a brassiere—the one he took off his female companion last night. Now he starts to grasp what has happened.

"Dammit, dammit! Goddammit, Christine! How did I let this happen?" He bangs his fist against the wall. "Why in the hell did she leave that brassiere in my car? Why? Why? I knew she was trouble. Now look!"

He stumbles to the kitchen table and plops down in a chair. His head is throbbing, but now it's not just from the alcohol he consumed last night.

One of Slick's favorite songs begins to play in his head; something about "Don't Go!" It's a song whose words ring hollow now—she's gone!

His thoughts turn to getting away—away from cotton picking, which he hates. He has thoughts about borrowing enough money from the bank to buy another car. Then he thinks he will head to Fort Huachuca, the army base located between Safford and Tucson. He will establish a taxi business that will drive soldiers back and forth to nearby towns along the route between Wilcox, Tucson, and even Safford, where they can have entertainment on weekends—including liquor and women—during their leave time. He imagines he will make a lot of money in fares and tips, more than he'll ever make in these cotton fields. Driving cars and having fun fit perfectly into his idea of being somebody, especially if you're your own boss.

After showering, he puts on his Sunday clothes—felt hat and all—takes one last look in the small wall mirror, and heads out the door. His destiny is calling. Remorse pushed aside, Carl is ready to answer.

Meanwhile, in the rearview mirror, Copply watches the miles of cotton fields fading from view. They are behind her now. After two hours of driving, just ahead of her headlights in the distance, the city lights of Tucson begin to appear. To Copply, the sight is both exciting and daunting. She has never lived in a city. She grips the wheel tightly, squints her eyes to focus her vision, and steps down harder on the gas pedal. She's apprehensive but not afraid; she's determined. Whatever lies ahead will be better than what she is leaving behind.

Nonetheless, she can't help feeling emotional as she tunes the car radio into a program featuring the famous Wings Over Jordan gospel choir, and they begin to sing a familiar gospel song: "He Knows How Much We Can Bear."

Copply wipes away a tear as she contemplates the reassurance that this song provides her in this moment. She can't help thinking about Sister Bessie. She briefly releases the steering wheel, lifts both hands in the air and shouts out loud, "Talk about pickin' in high cotton!"

PART
2

"Start where you are with what you've got. Make something of it, and never be satisfied."

(George Washington Carver)

Tucson and *Change*

It's early morning when Copply pulls into the yard of a small adobe structure with a door and two small front windows. She squints her eyes while reading a paper that bears the address.

"Yep, this is it."

She begins searching in her purse for the house key. She shakes the sleeping children.

"Come on! This is where we're gon' stay."

She gets out of the car and places the key in a heavy wooden door but finds it unlocked. It creaks loudly as she pushes it open. It's dark inside, and there is a strong, sickening smell that threatens to overwhelm her.

This first Tucson home for Copply and her children is located just east of South Park Avenue and north off Twenty-Second Street. It is very different from the compound of row-home apartments provided for cotton pickers they've known in Safford—very different!

"Pewww!" Carl Jr. bellows as he steps down into the room

where his mother is standing. He and Shirley grab their noses and quickly turn around to get back outside.

"This is definitely not what that real estate man described. This place is awful. I don't know if we can stay here."

"Hello, ma'am!" It is the deep voice of a young man in his late teens who has knocked lightly on the open door before stepping inside.

Copply is startled. She turns around quickly to face him.

"Who are you?"

"Oh, I didn't mean to scare you. My name is Emmett Haynes. I live in that house that's just across the alleyway from where you're parked. Are you planning to move in? If so, I'll be happy to help you get the place cleaned up. It's been vacant for a while."

Copply relaxes the tension in her shoulders as she reaches to shake Emmett's hand.

"My name is Copply. I can sure use some help. Those are my two kids outside. They're afraid to come inside, and they're too young to do much of the heavy work. What kinda house is this? The floors are dirt. The whole house is dirt."

"It's called *adobe*. The bricks that built this house are made of mud and straw. Arizona Indians used to build their houses this way. It's very strong."

"Why does it smell so bad in here?" Copply asks.

"Oh, I guess you weren't told that the lady who owned this house died—right there in that bed. They didn't find her for a week. That's why things are so messed up. Nobody has come back to clear out her things, strip the bedding, or empty the night jar—nothing has been done. It's gonna take a lot of work to make this place livable for you and those kids, but I'm volunteering my services. I'm between semesters in school, so I have some time on my hands."

"You're a godsend, Emmett. I was about to think I'd made a huge mistake but didn't know where else to go. Let me check on the kids. Then you can show me around the place. I'm sure they need to use the restroom. It's been a long drive getting here."

"Restroom? Oh, they didn't tell you about that either? The only running water is in the kitchen. There's no other indoor plumbing. There's an outdoor toilet, an outhouse, that sits over a cesspool—that's the restroom. Would you like to see it?"

Copply bucks her eyes in shock.

"What? We're used to bathing in tin tubs, but at least we had an inside toilet where we came from—this is gon' be rough! They will have to wait."

Emmett and Copply walk across the dirt floors to the kitchen, where there is a small sink with a dishpan full of dirty dishes.

"Well, this a good place for Junior to start helping." She looks around for something he can stand on to wash dishes.

They exit the house, and the tour continues through a patch of weeds to a tall, narrow wooden structure with a corrugated tin roof from which a metal pipe protrudes.

"This is the restroom."

Emmett grins while gingerly unlatching the door. He stands aside to allow Copply to peek inside. She sees what looks like a wooden bench with a large round hole in the middle. It stinks badly.

"Oh, my God! What have I got myself into? How will the kids ever manage this?"

Copply cannot ignore the sinking feeling she's getting in her gut.

Emmett follows her back into the house and searches for a broom and cloths to dust and wash dishes. He lifts the heavy, pungent night jar and heads for the outhouse to empty it. Copply goes to look for the children, who are playing hopscotch.

"Shirley, Junior, you two come in here! We have work to do. Now come on in."

She tugs at Junior's sleeve. Shirley holds on to his shirttail and follows.

"I've got some dishes for you to wash, Junior, just like Big Mama showed you. Shirley, here's a broom. You can sweep the floor. Don't push the dirt too hard; that will cause a lot of dust. Just brush real lightly, like this."

Copply demonstrates the sweeping technique for Shirley and hands her the broom. She pauses to observe the first few strokes, then nods her approval and moves on to the other work.

Work consists of changing the bedsheets, dusting the sparse furnishings, cleaning up the kitchen, and sweeping the floor into a neat pile of dirt to be discarded outside.

Emmett gives Copply directions to the closest grocery store, tells her the name of a neighbor who lives just a block away who keeps children in her home. He also introduces her to the idea of seeking work at the nearby Air Force base.

"You know, Miss Copply, you can probably get a job right away at Davis Monthan Air Base. I hear they're really needing workers, what with the war and all—especially in the kitchen. Lots of soldiers are coming in every day. My dad works there. He's a master chef. If you're interested, I'll tell him to talk to you. I'm sure he can get you hired."

"Emmett, that would be perfect. Yes, I'm very interested. Please tell him to come by with the information, even an application. That would be nice."

That evening, when things are finally straight enough to rest and after the kids and Copply have eaten the last of the food she packed, she lights the one kerosene lamp that she found in the house, washes their dusty feet and legs in an old enamel wash pan, and puts the children in the only bed. All three will sleep in it. The kids quickly fall asleep.

She finds a pen in her purse and fills out the job application that Emmett's father slipped under the door. She then searches her large purse for a writing tablet to write a letter to her parents:

Dear Daddy and Mother,

We made it safely to Tucson and have found a place to stay. It took a lot of work to move in, but we're all right now. A nice young man helped us. I'm applying for work on the air base here. I sure hope to get hired soon. The kids don't like this house, but it will have to do for now. A neighbor lady will keep them while I work, I hope!

I love you and miss you. Write me back at the address on the envelope.

Love,
Copply

Tomorrow will begin a new chapter in their lives. She has found the babysitter that Emmett told her about, and she has agreed to watch the children for a modest fee. When the children are secure in the neighbor's care, she will head out to get herself hired at the air base. A plan is coming together.

Leaving Carl Henry, the only lover she's ever known, and cotton picking, the only work she's ever known, is a quantum leap of faith, but that's exactly what she's doing. She is not afraid to seek a different life. It's wartime, and certain types of work on the air base are available here, even to Black people. This will be just what she needs.

"Wake up, you guys. Mama's goin' to find a job so we can stay here."

"Here?" Junior frowns his disapproval.

"Well, at least we're safe here for a while. Now get dressed. I want you to meet your new babysitter. Brush your teeth. Hurry!"

When the children are dressed, Copply hastily pulls on her sweater and hustles the kids into the car. The sitter that Emmett recommended is just a block away. She will be waiting.

Copply rushes back into the house, grabs the completed job application that she almost forgot off the kitchen table, and runs back to the car.

The introduction of Shirley and Junior to Mrs. Johnson is brief.

"What beautiful children!" Mrs. Johnson, a stout, brown-skinned, short woman, smiles broadly as she assists the children out of the car. "Come on in. I can't wait to get to know you!"

The children take halting steps into the house. It is much larger and more nicely furnished than the one they just left. There are large brightly colored chairs with pillows and a long beige sofa. There are toys in a big box in a corner of the room. The aroma of bacon wafts into the living room. As Copply looks on, the children politely and timidly sit on the edge of the sofa.

"Now, you guys be good. Mind Mrs. Johnson. I'll be back to pick you up as soon as I can. Mrs. Johnson is going to feed you. Use your good manners, you hear me?"

The children nod and say, "Yes ma-a-a-m."

Copply kisses them, thanks Mrs. Johnson for taking them on short notice, and exits the house for her car.

Copply is hired right away to work as a part-time short-order cook and part-time dishwasher in the Officers' Dining Hall. Perfect!

Two months later, Copply's father, Roger, decides to pack up and join her and his grandchildren. He and Daisy are separating. She is going back to Texas, according to a note that Copply receives from Pearlie Mae:

Hey Cope,

Just a note to tell you that Mr. Roger wants to let you know that he is leaving Safford and will be joining you in Tucson soon. Miss Daisy wants to go back to Texas. She will not be coming with him. I guess this means they are separating. So sorry. Please send him your address.

I miss you something terrible!

Your friend,
Pearlie

Now the space in the adobe house is way too small.

"With my father coming, there's not enough room for all

of us here," she tells Emmett as he's hanging over the rails of his back fence. "I'm going to need more space. Wish me luck."

Emmett gives her a thumbs-up and goes inside his house.

That night after work, Copply can hardly find her way home. A ferocious, blinding dust storm is blowing violently across the desert, enveloping streets and houses in dust. Copply runs into the home where the children are staying.

"Oh, my goodness, Mrs. Johnson, I've never seen anything like this before!"

Mrs. Johnson wraps Shirley and Junior in a blanket from head to feet and helps Copply shove them into the back seat of the car. She adjusts a towel around her own head and yells out loudly, "Thank God you don't have far to go. Be careful!"

She swiftly heads back inside. The children are too frightened to speak. They huddle close to Copply on the front car seat.

Once inside the house, Copply lights the kerosene lamp and rustles up some warm leftover soup for the evening meal. The howl of the wind is menacing. Suddenly, there's a loud crashing sound outside. Copply rushes to the window just in time to see the outhouse tumble to the ground. The children scream!

"Oh no, no, no, this can't be happening!" Copply tries not to sound panicked, but she is gripped in fear.

She hastily puts the frightened children to bed without washing their legs and feet and reassures them of their safety.

When they are finally asleep, she goes to the old overstuffed chair in the corner, sits down wearily, looks out at the toppled outhouse, and cries, burying her sobs in her hands. She doesn't want the children to hear her crying.

Copply takes the next day off from work to begin searching for a larger house, hopefully with indoor plumbing. She makes a left turn from Twenty-Second Street onto South Park Avenue. Three blocks south, she spots a "FOR RENT" sign. She stops and parks the car in front of it, walks up several wide steps, and knocks on the front door of a large pink stucco house.

"Yes" says the tall, handsome, brown-skinned man who introduces himself as Mr. Henderson, "I have a converted garage for rent just behind my house. Come, I'll show it to you."

When Copply sees the clean garage apartment, she can hardly contain her emotions. This is perfect and at a price she can afford. It has a large room with cement floors, four curtained front windows, and an entry door that faces Tyndall Avenue, a narrow dirt-alley-like street. It also has a large kitchen area with hot and cold running water and, most importantly, an indoor bathroom, complete with commode, wash basin, and a shower.

On seeing all this place offers, Copply screams, "Yes!"

She pays the landlord the first month's rent, gets the house key, and hurries to pick up the kids. She can't wait to tell them the good news.

"Come on, you guys. We have to pack up all of our stuff. We're moving!"

This is good news to the children. They hastily shove things into the car, anxious to see what will be their new home—almost as anxious as they are to see their favorite person in the whole wide world, Papa!

Renewal

When Roger arrives, after the first hour of hugs and gleeful babble, Copply gets down to business.

"Daddy, let me help you fill out a base application. I know they'll hire you. You're a good worker."

"All right, but just be sure we're on the same shift. We only have one good car—mine is on its last leg."

Copply laughs at this remark. She is so happy to be back with her father again. He's equally happy to be near her and the children. He tickles and plays with them. Laughter and screams of childish delight are heard as they leap onto his lap and on his back.

Roger is a churchgoing man. He encourages Copply to attend services at the little storefront Baptist church that he has found downtown and insists on taking the children to Sunday school. They like going anywhere with Papa.

"Now, don't you get those clothes dirty," Copply admonishes as they race to get in the front seat with Papa.

"It's my turn to sit by the window," Junior insists as the two scuffle, pushing and shoving.

"You sat there last Sunday!" squeals Shirley, tuning up her face to cry.

"All right, don't make me cut off one of these mesquite switches before we even leave home," Roger says in a loud, deep, scolding voice.

Neither child wants to feel the familiar sting of Papa's switch on their legs. They become quiet. Shirley meekly slides in the middle near Papa, and Junior once again gets the window seat. He gleefully rests his elbow on the open window sill, imitating Papa. Shirley pokes her lip out in a pout.

Roger eventually convinces Copply to come with him and the kids to church. When she's seated, the choir begins to sing a fast-paced gospel song: " I'm Walking Up the King's Highway!"

There is clapping and shouts of "amen" in the audience. Sister Sadie, eighty-five years old, rises from her aisle pew, grabs her walking cane, and begins stepping lively in the aisle to the cadence of the song.

Copply smiles broadly as she strains to see how the children are behaving in the seats closer to the front. They are giggling and pointing mockingly at Sister Sadie. Copply rises and moves to a seat directly behind them. When they feel her thump on their heads, they turn, surprised to see their mother's stern-looking face. They know to stop the misbehavior.

"She started it!" Junior whispers across his shoulder.

Attending church services on Sundays helps Copply meet new people and enjoy the spirit of the church as she also becomes familiar with city life. Although Carl Henry is now living in Tucson too, they are divorcing. She is a single woman. She meets several single men on the base and in town, but none of them interests her as much as a young deacon she meets in the church.

Matthew Hill is a tall, light-skinned man who captivates Copply with his singing and his ability to move church-goers with fervent prayers, which he delivers in loud, emotional cadence. These skills make him very popular around town. He is often invited to lead services in other churches.

One day, he and Copply strike up a conversation after church.

"Mr. Hill, I must tell you how moved I am by your singing. I love the way you sing 'Precious Memories.' That's one of my favorites. I've never heard such a strong, moving deliverance of a song."

"Much obliged, Ma'am. May I please know your name?"

"My name is Copply. I'm Deacon Roger's daughter."

"Oh, now that's a good recommendation! He's a fine Christian man. My first name is Matthew. You can call me that if you like, although most people just call me Hill. Guess 'Matthew' twists the tongue too much."

They both laugh.

"I like the short version myself. I'll call you Hill too."

"Are those your two fine children?"

"Yes. Do you have any?"

"No. Never been married. Where is your husband?"

"We're in the process of divorcing, but he lives here in town."

"In that case, perhaps you and I might get to know each other better over dinner. Are you available next Saturday evening? There's a good barbeque place in town."

"Sure. Here's my address. I'll be ready at five. Daddy will watch the children for me, I'm sure."

The attraction between the two is obvious to all observers—and there are more than a few of them. They begin dating steadily. After a couple of months, they announce to the church and to Roger their intent to get married. Roger professes pleasure but can't hide his skepticism about the haste of this decision.

A letter comes announcing that Copply's birth mother, Earlee; her stepfather, Charles Jackson; and her sister, Rosetta, are moving to Tucson and will need to stay with her. Things are getting very tight in the new house. Something has to change—soon.

A wedding takes place in City Hall without witnesses—no family, no friends, just a judge and a county clerk. The Hill couple move into a rooming house near downtown that is managed by Mr. Hill's uncle, Reverend Sam Alfred Dabner, who is also the pastor of the church.

The area is inhabited by an assortment of low-income residents, mostly comprised of poor Blacks, but there are also some Asian and Mexican apartment dwellers in the mix. It is located just one block from one of the city's most popular, and often dangerous, Black adult entertainment centers—Meyers Street. Loud music, gambling, liquor drinking, and prostitution characterize Meyers Street's ambience on any given night, but Saturday nights are the most likely to erupt in some form of violence; fights over women, money, and territory occur with regularity, resulting in stabbings, shootings, and sometimes deaths.

It is on one such Saturday night that Copply is awakened to answer a call on the rooming house's single communal telephone. It is an emergency call from St. Mary's Hospital. Carl Henry, who also lives near Meyers Street in Sabino Alley, has been shot by his live-in girlfriend—five bullet shots to his stomach. Copply, stunned and scared, gasps, drops the phone, mumbles something about an emergency to Matthew, hastily pulls on an old dress and shoes, and rushes out to drive to the hospital.

Once there, she's led into a room where Carl lies unconscious but alive. She is told he needs a blood transfusion if he is to have a chance to survive. She volunteers for a test of her blood to see if her type matches his. It does. She gives five pints of her blood to Carl. His life is spared. This near-death episode is sobering for Carl. When he leaves the hospital, he begins to live a more chaste, upright life.

For his part, Roger buys a small corrugated tin house on Tyndall Avenue across the street from the garage apartment where he has lived with Copply and the kids. For now, the kids live with him while the new couple gets situated in the place downtown. The rest of the family stays in the garage apartment. Charles, Copply's stepfather, secures work in the Base cafeteria. Rosetta and Earlee work as maids in private homes.

The smell of kerosene and biscuits baking awakens the kids, who have slept with Papa in a wide, low bed.

"Papa, I'm hungry," Junior stammers, wiping his eyes. "I'm also cold. Shirley wet the bed *again!*" His frown registers his aggravation.

"Well, wrap a towel around you and sit near the stove. Breakfast is almost ready. Do you smell that bacon? We gon' have some biscuits with butter and syrup, bacon, and a cold glass of milk. Don't that sound good? Wake your sister up."

Junior leans way over—just far enough to pull one of Shirley's braids.

"Get up, sleepyhead who pees in the bed. It's time to eat."

Major *Change*

The rooming house is a cavernous building that was once a bakery with very high ceilings. Rooms are partitioned with six-foot drywall panels that provide minimal privacy. Shirley, age five, and Junior, seven, sleep together in one of the rooms. They are playful and irreverent of the needs of adults for quiet time.

"Stop pulling the cover off of me!" Junior yells.

"Move your cold feet!" Shirley protests loudly.

Miss McJunkins, whose room is next to theirs, yells, "Be quiet! Hush!" several times every night.

The kids giggle and lower their voices slightly. They're not sleepy. Lights have to be turned off early because it's a wartime rule in the city. These kids still have plenty of energy. Some nights, they slip out of bed and go to sit in the large window near their room to watch the searchlights beaming from the Air Base high overhead, scouring the dark skies in search of enemy aircraft that might be lurking over the city. Nothing ever happens.

Copply isn't used to sharing space with strangers. She pleads with Hill to move away into a house.

"We need to move. I don't like this place. It isn't good for the kids. There are too many unfamiliar adults coming in and out. I'm not comfortable with this situation."

Matthew resists. He is satisfied. He is diabetic and enjoys the safety of always having a roof over his head with his uncle.

"They'll be all right—just give them time."

When he is offered a job at Shamrock Dairy, Copply insists that he take it.

"This is our opportunity. Take the job."

The dairy is located outside of Tucson's city limits in a small, sparsely settled community called Jaynes Station. It was once a train way-station where freight cars switched tracks. It is a short distance away but not too far for Copply to commute to her new job as a waitress in a prestigious restaurant in town. Best of all, workers at the dairy are provided nice houses to live in with indoor plumbing, kitchens, and two bedrooms.

"This is the best house I've ever lived in!" Copply exclaims, gleefully clapping her hands as their sparse furnishings are being placed in each room by volunteer movers from the church. "Thank y'all so much! Here's some lemonade to cool you down."

The next day, Copply takes the children to enroll in their new school. It doesn't really look like a school—just two abandoned freight cars on an old, unused rail track. This is the school for all kids who live in the Jaynes Station area, regardless of age or race.

Copply and the children approach the door cautiously, stepping high to get up onto the first step of the boxcar. This is definitely different from Tucson's segregated Dunbar Elementary and Junior High School that the children have attended in Tucson!

"Mama, are you sure we're in the right place?" Junior whispers.

Copply tugs hard at the door until it opens, then pulls Shirley up by the hand.

"Good morning. Welcome," says the tall, slender white woman who greets them. She smiles at the children. "I'm Miss McHenry. I teach here with my sister."

This is the first time the children will be taught by white teachers, two sisters who teach all the grades in the boxcar school. It is orderly, and the students are racially diverse. Although schools in Arizona are supposed to be racially segregated, segregation is impractical here—there are too few students. Copply is very happy with all of these features. Life is opening up beyond her wildest imagination.

"Now y'all mind these teachers. Don't make me have to come up here. Get your lessons and shut your mouths, do you hear me?"

She kisses the children and goes back home to change into

a Moroccan-motif waitress uniform consisting of a colorful striped headdress, white tailored blouse, and matching striped long skirt. She checks herself in the mirror. Her slender body looks elegant in it. This is a far cry from her drab, oversized, masculine-looking cotton-field clothes. Her job now is at the Studio Patio, an upscale restaurant back in Tucson, where tourists congregate.

At home, Shirley's favorite playmate is a white boy, younger than she, who lives on her street. His are the only parents who will permit their child to play with her. They ride bicycles and play hide-and-seek between the trees after school.

"Can you come out to play?" is always replied to with an enthusiastic "Yes!"

Six months after the move to Shamrock Dairy, Matthew is fired for having a diabetic seizure on the job. Though he is a good worker, his health is hazardous to others. It is with great disappointment that the family packs up and leaves, this time for Marana, a place even farther west of Tucson, where there are miles of cotton fields. The commute to her job in Tucson is too far for Copply now. She is forced to quit and follow Matthew to Marana to pick cotton—*again*.

"This is not what I expected," she confides to a new acquaintance. "I came a long way out of Safford's cotton patches just to end up back in another one. Things have got to change!"

Besides the misery she feels about this setback, she is beginning to see a side of Matthew that she never noticed before. It's a side she doesn't like. He is duplicitous, superficial, and religiously hypocritical. She has caught him in lies, mostly about money, and his temper is anything but that of a true Christian. A fissure in the marriage begins to form.

Roger misses the children. It isn't long before he locks up his tin shack in Tucson and joins the family to pick cotton. They find a place where all of them can live cheaply.

"Reverend Baker, do you have a space that we can rent? There's five of us, two kids and three grown folks."

Copply uses her most serious voice to convince the owner of the building. It is a large building that houses the town's only small café where Black cotton pickers are allowed to eat and use the restrooms.

"Come with me. I'll show you the only space I have left."

The short, portly, Rev. Baker leads Copply outside and up a steep set of stairs. When he opens the door, she is dismayed.

There is a single room. It's just large enough for two beds and two different night jars. Matthew and Copply will sleep in one, Papa and the kids in the other; no privacy.

"Oh, my God!" Copply mumbles under her breath. "This is worse than any other place we've lived—no privacy, no bathroom, no indoor running water, and no kitchen. But it will have to do for now. Nothing else is available."

Each night, at Papa's direction, the two children kneel

beside the bed and recite the Lord's Prayer out loud: *"Our Father, which art in heaven, hallowed be thy name. Thy kingdom come. Thy will be done, on earth as it is in heaven. Give us this day our daily bread and forgive us our debts as we forgive our debtors. And lead us not into temptation"*—Junior leans heavily against Shirley's shoulder, nudging her over—*"but deliver us from evil."* Another nudge by Junior. *"For thine is the kingdom, and the power, and the glory, forever and ever."*

Junior bolts up before *amen* is finished to secure his place on the right side of the bed, assuring that Shirley will have to sleep in the middle between him and Papa.

"That's not fair!" Shirley shrieks every time—to no avail.

When Matthew and Copply think the children are asleep, they move into positions in their bed to enjoy a few moments of intimacy. The bedsprings squeak. Muffled moaning sounds are heard. Shirley places her fingers in her ears and tries to go to sleep.

Both Shirley and Junior are old enough to go to the cotton fields now. They have burlap croaker sacks to use for their pickings on Saturdays. When they are full, they are emptied into one or the other adult's sack, and the picking starts over again.

On weekdays, the children attend classes in the area's only school for "colored" students, a one-room building with water and a toilet. One teacher, Mrs. Katherine Maxwell, wife of Dunbar's principal, Morgan Maxwell, teaches all grades from first to twelfth. Her system is flawless: through instructional rotation and peer tutoring, all students are served. It is a model of the phrase "Each one, teach one." Students are orderly and studious—they have no choice in Mrs. Maxwell's classes! If he could, Junior would prefer to be in the cotton fields listening to the men's stories and jokes. Sometimes Papa talks Copply into letting him skip school.

Copply's dissatisfaction with the direction of her life grows. She discovers how different Matthew is at home from how he is at church. He is petulant and critical at home, never satisfied, and excessively strict with the children. At church, he is jovial and enjoys accolades from members about his prayers that elicit loud "amens" and shouts of "hallelujah" from the women. The dissonance is stark and troublesome.

When the two-week Christmas break from school begins, Copply takes the kids into Tucson for a visit. From a friend, she learns about a house on the east side that is being sold by a Black Pullman Porter. He is retiring from the railroad job and going home to his family in Chicago. Copply contacts him and arranges to see the small, three-room stucco adobe house on South Campbell Boulevard. The asking price of $2,000 is above her means, but she bargains with the owner to take a down payment of the money she has saved and allow her to make payments on the balance. He agrees and signs over the house to her.

When Copply tells Matthew what she has done, he is less than enthusiastic.

"How you gon' pay for that house?" he growls. "Cain't you ever be satisfied?" His face reddens with anger.

Copply ignores him. She begins gathering up clothes and the household items they've brought to Marana. She finds boxes and bags downstairs to put them into.

"Goodbye, old rags. I won't need you anymore—ever," she says, tossing her men's pants and shirt in a trash barrel outside the door. "You too!" she exclaims while throwing away a pair of muddy boots.

By the time the workday is over and Roger is back at home, she is ready to move out. She tells her father of her abrupt plans, emphasizing her good luck to find and purchase a house on the "white" side of town.

"That's good news, baby girl. Now I can go home, too."

Different but the *Same*

City life appeals to Copply. She enjoys the buzz of traffic noise and the convenience of many types of stores. She applies and is hired at the local Young Women's Christian Association (YWCA), where, as a maid, she maintains the upstairs living quarters—residences of young career women, most of whom are here from other states. It is a large, well-established organization run by women executives that mainly serves the social and recreational needs of middle-class white women. It feels safe and friendly to Copply. The young women residents often shower her with cast-off clothes, toiletries, books, and magazines. She alters many of the clothing items to fit Shirley as she grows and matures—big savings to her budget.

Dunbar Elementary and Junior High is the school for the children. It is a segregated school for Black students, across town from the family's new home on South Campbell Avenue. Shirley rides as far as the Y with Copply, then walks the rest of the distance, about a mile, to school. Junior rides his bicycle to school because he needs it for his evening paper route, which he works after school. He loves this means of making money far better than picking cotton. Shirley is very happy to be back at Dunbar with her friends. She proudly shows Copply her first report card.

"Look, Mama, all A's—well, almost. I got a C in arithmetic."

Copply takes the card for a closer look.

"You did well in English and Geography. I don't understand why you're so dumb in math. That was always my favorite subject. I could out-figure the kids who were two and three grades ahead of me. That's how I finished school when I was only fifteen—they kept skipping me up a grade every year. I guess you got your numbers brain from your father; it sure wasn't from me!"

Shirley lowers her head at this remark. It takes the wind out of her sails.

Marana is a place Shirley can't ever forget. It is etched in her youthful memory. She vividly remembers the sight of miles of rows of cotton and how it smells when it's wet and sticky.

One day in class, she draws a picture of her family picking cotton—everybody is in it: Mama, Mr. Hill, Junior, herself, and Papa. It gets displayed by her teacher on a wall in the hall. A local newspaper reporter visiting the school notices it and takes a picture of it with Mr. Maxwell and Shirley posing, looking up at it. He posts it in the *Tucson Daily Star*, the city's largest newspaper. The Y staff and residents see it and congratulate Copply.

"Look, Copply, here's your daughter in the newspaper. You must be so proud."

It is the first time Copply has seen the picture. Her chest swells with pride—her kid is in the paper! She begins to pay closer attention to Shirley's drawings. She buys coloring books for her to use at home. This is an activity that Shirley loves. There are no children her age to play with in this neighborhood, either. She spends a lot of time reading library books, coloring, and listening to sitcom stories on the radio. Her favorites are *I Love Lucy*, *Amos 'n' Andy*, *The Roy Rogers Show*, and *The Gene Autry Show*.

In late 1950, Tucson's executive school board members vote to end school segregation. Dunbar and all of the city's public schools are to be racially integrated in the fall of 1951. This means that Shirley, now an eighth grader, will change schools once again. Junior will graduate with the last Dunbar class and move on to high school. This news is unsettling on many levels—to Tucson's Black community in general and to Shirley specifically.

"Mama, I'm scared. I don't want to leave my teachers and my friends. When will I get to see them?"

"Don't worry, baby, things will work out." Copply says these words confidently, trying not to show her true skepticism and doubt.

Mixed with its good parts are bad parts: the sense of Black pride and security that characterize Dunbar school are on the chopping block. Not only will students be dispersed to attend different schools in their geographic home neighborhoods, but the name of the historically significant school for Black students, Paul Laurence Dunbar, will be changed to that of a white person's. This last point is the most distasteful of all that is changing. Paul Laurence Dunbar, a lauded post-slavery Black poet, is revered nationwide by Black folks. How can they just erase his significance in this community with the stroke of a pen?

The school is recognized citywide for sports dominance, award-winning marching bands, a renowned student chorus, and a reputation for academic excellence. For some, integration is the worst thing that could happen; others view it as a change long awaited.

"We won't have it!" the preacher shouts loudly from the pulpit during Sunday's church service.

Copply and Matthew attend parent meetings called by Mr. Maxwell to air parent and community protests as well as affirmations supporting the new policy.

"I'm not sending my kids to no white school. This is a good enough school right here!" exclaims an angry female parent, stamping her foot and pointing downward.

"What if those white teachers don't treat our kids right?

Who's gonna be there to watch out for them?" asks a soft-spoken father.

"If one of them white kids calls my son a nigger, I'm gonna tell him to pick up something and knock the shit out of him! What they gonna do then? Expel him? Then I'll have to get into it!" says one agitated, red-faced father.

"Aw, don't y'all be so negative. This might turn out to be the best thing for our kids. They need to learn about other races. They'll need that for the future. The world is changing. We have to change with it. That's what's best for our kids," reasons a calmer, older man.

Loud, approving applause is heard from the audience.

The two-hour meeting begins to dissipate in emotional intensity, with sentiment in favor of the change seeming to carry the day. Copply mingles, exchanging comments with parents. Matthew leaves her and walks alone to the car.

Finally, after all the talk, the die is cast—schools will no longer be segregated. When school starts in September, 1951, Shirley walks from her home directly to a nearby school. She enrolls in the eighth grade at Mansfeld Junior High, a prestigious school on East Sixth Street, across from the campus of the University of Arizona.

As she timidly pulls open the heavy front doors, she is unaware that she is the only Black student to enroll that day and that she is the first and only Black girl who will attend during the two years there. Copply does not accompany her daughter. Shirley is on her own to navigate her new experience. She must pull her own cotton sack.

Shirley's Voice

After many days of anxiety, fear, and undeniable knots in my stomach, I braced my thirteen-year-old self and entered the giant doors of Mansfeld Junior High School on the first day of school in Tucson, Arizona. The year was 1951. The Black community that I'd grown up in had demanded change: more equitable educational opportunity, better books—as in new, not old, worn-out, handed down from white schools—better athletic equipment, and so on. That change was finally granted by the Tucson Unified School District's board of trustees. In a sweeping decision, it voted to integrate the schools, to allow all students to attend schools within walking distance of their homes, and, while they were at the "change" thing, to change the name of Paul Laurence Dunbar School to John Springs School. It would no longer be named after a Black son of slaves but after a white son of pioneers. This name change was not what Black citizens expected. It was not the change they wanted—not at all! There was much protesting, but it was to no avail.

For the better part of a century, Dunbar School in Tucson had been the sole source of formal education and socialization for Black kids in the first through ninth grades. There was more than a little sentiment surrounding this change—not just for me but for scores of other students, parents, Black citizens, and political leaders.

Brown vs. the Board of Education, the landmark school desegregation case, was just making its way onto the Supreme Court's docket to be argued by Thurgood Marshall for the plaintiffs, litigated, and decided. The Tucson Board of Education, by integrating its schools in 1950, was way ahead of the game. Not every one of the white people in the town, including many of the teachers, was in favor of this move either, but it took place without much rancor. District teachers, both white and Black, were reassigned as deemed necessary, and schools throughout the district received new, racially diverse students.

Beginning this year, I would be the lone Black student on a campus comprised of approximately three hundred predominantly white students, many wealthy, and their white teachers—that was Mansfeld Junior High School, located across the street from the University of Arizona's football stadium in Tucson, Arizona. There would be no more busing of Black or any other students to Dunbar Elementary and Junior High School.

My foray into this "foreign" territory was characterized by reluctance, fear, and anxiety—to say the least. There was a lot riding on my back. I was a token in a large social experiment; mixing Black and white students in their formative years—that just *had* to work. I was not handpicked to attend this upscale school, it just happened to be within my natural attendance area because of the location of our small home on that side of town. It was indeed within walking distance, but for me, it might just as well have been the distance between my house and Mars! There was no one to walk to school with, to share my feelings with. None of the kids who attended Mansfeld lived where I lived—south of Broadway on Campbell Avenue. There were only a handful of Blacks and a few retired Mexicans in my neighborhood. At age thirteen, this would be the challenge of my life!

Although I'd been taught by Morgan Maxwell, our illustrious principal, and the teachers at Dunbar to "Be the Best," heretofore, my world had been all-Black: parents, family friends, church acquaintances, and school-related relationships such as teachers, classmates, the principal, school secretary, choir master, and even the custodians. I had been held in high regard in this world, where I was a high achiever. I was fully aware of expectations for my success in life but didn't feel any undue pressure to attain it. I always felt confident that I could hit the mark; I was smart, friendly, and relatively attractive. Now my trailblazing experiences in this new setting would be closely monitored. Mine was a unique experience among my peers. Hopes were high for exceptional accomplishments on my part. I was a drum majorette of sorts, leading change and being watched by many. I didn't want to let them down. Nevertheless, I couldn't quiet the trepidation I felt.

Jim Crow laws and practices in Tucson had conditioned me toward a certain kind of hesitancy in the presence of white people—it was representative of a subtle brand of fear. Things were separate and not always equal. There were different forms of retribution to be paid for infringements. But most of all, the message conveyed was that Blacks were somehow inferior to the whites in that town. Although there were no "white only" signs posted, as one would commonly see in the South, separation was quite the order in theaters and restaurants and at lunch counters. We were not "good enough" to share those spaces was the message. Now here I was, like a fly in the ointment, at a school where I was so noticeably the only different one. I was so afraid I wouldn't be "good enough." It was the first time I'd felt that way.

Boosting my flagging self-esteem took more than just my family and friends. To that end, I owe so very much to some of the white people in Mansfeld who witnessed my demurring behavior and reached out to lift me up: Principal Andy Anderson; PE teachers like Coach Johnson; the choir teacher, Mr. Sayers; friendly students like Leona, Judy, Peggy, Martha, Marcia, Irma, Terry, Deanna, Dick, Bob, Phil, and others; and especially Ms. Gracie Hirleman, my English teacher. One day, she yanked me to the proverbial curb and told me to get my head up and to start believing in myself. She said I was smart; "As smart as any of these white kids." Her words, and the finger she shook in my face while she talked to me, were stinging to my wounded soul—forcing embarrassing tears from my eyes. Her belief in me and the courage to confront me about my self-pitying, slacking behavior were what turned me around at Mansfeld. I was despondent from missing my Dunbar friends and was slacking in my school work—my grades showed it. She called me out for it. I was both angered and energized by her words. That day, I determined to be a new person—to show 'em who I *really* was and what I had brought with me from Dunbar. It was a much-needed scolding from someone I had come to respect. I didn't want to disappoint her.

I went on to excel in all areas of student life in that all-white-except-me school. I not only survived but thrived academically and socially. The experiment worked, and I, as well as all those white people around me—teachers, students, parents, and administrators—all of us were the better for it. This was the launching pad for my future dreams: attending college, becoming a school teacher and a campus leader, acquiring the highest academic degree in my field, leading school change at the state level, and, yes, living an affluent life of my own. It was the first instance, but not the last, in which random interventions by goodhearted people of the opposite race, like Ms. Hirleman, have changed the trajectory of my life.

Turning *Point*

When Shirley crosses the graduation stage in 1953 to receive an award for making straight A's in math, science, Spanish, and all of the other courses taken in her last year at Mansfeld Junior High School, Copply is in the audience. Her pride is palpable. She claps loudly, smiling up at Shirley, who is on her way to high school with good scholarship and many new friends—most of whom are not Black.

Copply thinks of Pearlie and Sister Bessie. How she wishes they were sitting there with her to see this! When she gets back home, she finds pen and paper to write a letter to Pearlie.

Dear Pearl,

I'm writing to tell you how much I miss you here in Tucson. I have finally bought a little house. It's not fancy, but it's the best that I can afford right now. I love my job at the YWCA—everyone there is so nice to me. The kids are growing up nicely. I watched Shirley graduate from junior high school today—yes, she's now a teenager!

She is Student of the Year in a school where she is the only Black student. I am so proud! I kept wishing that you could be sitting next to me. You would have been so proud, too. I hope we will see each other soon. Give the kids hugs and kisses from me. I know Mary Beth is a little lady now. I hope she's helping you.

Give my best to Sister Bessie and any of the girls who are still there. More later.

Love,
Copply

The fissure in the marriage of Copply and Matthew that began to erupt in Marana is now a full-blown crack. Copply's assertive, ambitious personality feels abrasive to Matthew. He resents her. Copply, on the other hand, begins to view Matthew as feckless due to his inability to maintain a steady income. She is the breadwinner. Tension is elevated between them. They have loud arguments. The kids stay away from home as much as possible to avoid the bickering.

After moving back from Marana, during the years that Copply and the kids are busily making tracks in their new world, Roger leaves Tucson to try his hand at logging work in the Northwest—Oregon. It pays good money, and the weather is cool. He works for a lumber company, sawing logs into planks. The work is hard and dusty. While there, he contracts tuberculosis. He returns to Tucson a sick man, unable to work or take care of himself. Within a short time, he succumbs to the serious lung disease and dies in St. Mary's Hospital.

The day the hospital calls and tells Copply that her beloved father, Roger, is dead, her whole world comes crashing thunderously down. Copply sits on the sofa holding the newly installed telephone, unable to comprehend the words she hears. How can he be gone? Her father is the rock that she leans on. How can he be gone? He's only fifty-two years old—gone so soon? She dissolves in grief-filled tears. Shirley rushes to embrace and hold her. Her mother shudders and cries uncontrollably.

"No, my daddy can't be gone! No, no!"

She collapses backward onto the pillows, wailing and sobbing. Shirley sees her mother cry for the first time. She doesn't cry with her. She feels angry—angry at whoever did this to her Papa. How dare they take him away! How *dare* they!

What does this mean for Copply and her children? It's a question she can't bear to contemplate in this moment. She must get up, arrange a funeral, and bury her rock.

With Roger's passing, Matthew is more emboldened in his disputes with Copply. Not only does the crack in their relationship widen, now there are jagged edges that often erupt in physical fighting. He doesn't like her disparaging remarks about his hypocritical behavior—how he's different at church from his demeanor with her and the kids at home.

Nor does he like her goading him to look for work that will pay the bills.

"Shut up!" he bellows loudly.

She ignores him—continues with her frustrated rant, digging in deeper and deeper.

"A lot of other men take care of their wives and kids. I know some women who don't have to get up and go to a job every day. I should have married one of those men!"

Whap! He throws a slap to her face. Now the fight is on. Copply is not one to back down. She fights back, throwing punches into his midsection. He picks her up and carries her to their bed, where he flings her down and proceeds to hit her as if he's giving her a spanking. She kicks and screams, fighting back with all she has.

"Get off of me! Leave me alone!" She claws at his arms and face, attempting to scratch him with her fingernails.

Eventually, he backs off and goes outside to cool off in the backyard. Copply doesn't cry. She just straightens her clothes and thinks about her next move. To her embarrassment, she sees the neighbors on two sides and across the street gathered together talking. She knows they are talking about the loud commotion they have overheard. Thankfully, the children are not at home this time.

Her thoughts go to her father. If he were alive, he would intervene and stop Matthew from abusing her. Carl Henry had his faults, but he never hit her. This marriage is definitely a mistake. She has no desire to stay with him.

"I've got to get out of here! Some way, somehow, I'm gonna leave this crazy man!"

The next week, something miraculous happens: While shopping in the Safeway Market near her job, Copply meets a white woman in the produce section of the store. The two strangers strike up a conversation about life in general that becomes specific to Copply's current situation. She pours out her burdensome marital problems to the lady, who listens with a sympathetic ear. When the conversation ends, Copply goes to the checkout stand. The lady she has been talking with hastens toward her, extending a white envelope.

"This is for you. Don't open it until you get home."

Copply thanks her, places the envelope in her purse, finishes checking out, and gets into her car to drive home. Once the groceries are put away, she remembers the envelope, retrieves it from her purse, and sits down on the couch to read what she expects to be a letter. To her amazement, the envelope contains ten twenty-dollar bills and a small piece of paper that says, "God bless you!" Copply is speechless. Tears form in her eyes. This is the answer she needs.

"Thank you, dear God!" She prays a tearful prayer of thanksgiving and begins plotting her escape—once again.

That night, she calls Carl Henry to advise him of her plans to leave town and asks him to assume care of Shirley, who is now a sophomore in high school, until she can send for her.

Junior no longer lives at home. He lives somewhere near Meyers Street with someone she doesn't know. He left the last time she and Matthew fought. Matthew drove him away when Junior attempted to intervene and stop him from hitting his mother.

"Carl, I need your help. I've got to leave here. I'm leaving Matthew. I can't take any more of his ways. He's taken to hitting me—in front of the kids. You know I'm not taking that. It's time to go. Me and the kids deserve better. I'm leaving for California tomorrow morning. Shirley wants to stay here in Tucson. She's doing so well in school. I want to leave her here until I get settled out there. So, I'm calling to ask you to take her for the rest of this school year. She won't be any trouble. Can you do that? If so, I'll get her packed up, and you can pick her up after school tomorrow. I'll explain this to her tonight."

"Wow, this is a sudden move! Are you sure you want to go all the way to California by yourself? Do you know anybody out there?"

"Yes, Daddy's sister, Aunt Rosie, lives in Brawley. I'll stay with her for a day or two on the way. Then I'll go on to my cousin Ozella's place in LA. I'm sure I can stay with her awhile. I'll find work and get my own place by the time school is out. Then I'll send for Shirley. Junior is already living on his own somewhere downtown. You might want to check on him—he's pretty wild right now. I think he might join the Navy—he's talked about it."

"Okay." Carl's long, low sigh communicates his concerned reservation. "Tell Shirley to look for me. I'll honk when I get there. And don't you worry. Just take care of yourself—I'll take care of Shirley. Good luck!"

Copply avoids Matthew that night. Her plans are becoming quite clear in her mind. Tomorrow she will make her move. She picks up the phone when the coast is clear and calls a cousin who lives in Los Angeles, California.

"Ozella? This is your cousin Copply—Uncle Roger's daughter. Yes, it's been a long time. The kids are fine, thank you. Look, Ozella, I'm coming out there next week—maybe as early as Monday or Tuesday. Do you have a place where I can stay for a short while until I find a job and can get a place of my own? It's just me for now. The kids are staying in Arizona. You do? Oh, praise God! Well, look for me. I'm coming your way!"

The cousins conclude the conversation with Copply jotting down Ozella's address and a few directions to her home.

Carl Henry can be counted on to pick up Shirley. He will explain what's happening and take her to the safety of his home, located way south of Twenty-Second Street on what was once an Indian reservation. Shirley won't be happy that her mother is leaving, but she will enjoy the peace and attention in store for her with her father.

Copply's heart is filled with sorrow over this separation from her children. They have been through a lot together. This is just one more tear in the fabric of her life, but she's determined to make the most of it. She will drive her destiny from now on, relying on herself—not a man. She's determined to live a free life, unfettered either by harsh Jim Crow laws and customs or by the unreasonable whims and demands of an undeserving man. Her sense of self-efficacy is strong. She can do this for herself and her children.

When Matthew leaves for work the next morning, Copply shoves as many clothes as she can into her small suitcase, grabs her purse with $200 in it, closes the front door, gets into the 1949 Ford coupe parked beside the house, and backs it onto the street headed north. She will turn it toward Highway 10 and head west—all the way to Los Angeles. She grips the wheel firmly, sits back in the driver's seat, and steps on the gas—once again.

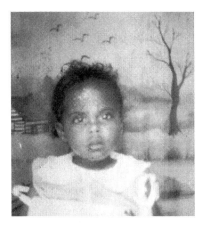

Shirley Sprinkles at approximately two years old.

Copply Williams Robinson when she was about nineteen years old.

Shirley's handsome father at approximately twenty-six years old. He was likely dressed up for a singing performance at church.

Shirley's grandfather, "Papa."

Shirley's brother, Carl Junior, with Shirley and their mother,
Copply, at Shirley's second wedding ceremony.

Carl Henry later in life.

Mama with her third (and last) husband,
Johnny Faulk.

PART

3

"Life is not about how many times you fall down. It's about how many times you get back up."

(Jaime Escalante)

A Brand-New *World*

Ozella's home is spacious, warm, and inviting. After the five-hundred-mile drive from Tucson, Copply welcomes a warm bath and a good home-cooked meal. Although she is exhausted from the trip, she and Ozella spend a couple of hours talking. It has been years since they've seen each other. They talk about the issues that bring her to California and about Copply's prospects for a job. Ozella's husband, a minister, sits with them and listens in. Before going to bed, Ozella hands her a *Los Angeles Times* newspaper and shows her where to find the Classified Ads. There might be a job available in there.

The next morning, Copply rises early, anxious to scan the classifieds in search of a job. When Ozella gets up, Copply asks her about a place called Von's Market. There is a waitress job available there. She's sure that after her experience working at the Studio Patio in Tucson, she can qualify for it. Ozella encourages her to apply and gives her driving directions to the store's location in the Crenshaw shopping area. Copply eats a hasty breakfast of dry cereal, irons her best dress, and gets ready to check out the job opening.

When she arrives at her destination, Copply is shocked to see how crowded the huge parking lots are that surround the market. Seeing that many people in one place is intimidating. She braces herself, checks her hemline to be sure her slip isn't showing, and walks calmly into the store.

To her surprise, what she thought would be a restaurant turns out to be a snack bar located in the front of the huge grocery store, near the entrance. It is a long, curved counter with about twenty bar stools. Someone in a white jacket is moving about behind a wall, handing platters of food to a group of waitresses through a square hole in the wall. The women are barking orders to that person while attaching pieces of paper to a rotating wheel-like fixture that suspends from a midpoint in the window. It is a scene that Copply finds fascinating, but she wonders if she can do this kind of waitress work. It's fast paced, catering to people who are in a hurry.

"I'm here to apply for a job," she calls out to one of the waitresses, who has stopped near where she's standing to serve a customer. Her voice is loud to override the store noise.

"Patrick, get out here. A lady wants to apply for the job!"

Patrick steps out and beckons Copply to come through the swinging door to his office behind the kitchen. After answering a few questions, Copply walks out of the kitchen with a green uniform and an apron across her arm. She is hired and told to go to the restroom in back of the store, get dressed in the uniform, and report to work. She starts working on her first California job right away. Her joy is hard to contain.

Copply learns the work quickly. She enjoys meeting all the customers. Many of them are celebrities whom she has either heard of or seen on TV. She's quick, amicable, and pretty. She is also a cashier, depositing money from customers and counting back change. This is a new skill. She learns it quickly. She is in a whole new world—one that she will certainly master. She can see her rainbow forming. Change is on the horizon.

She earns a lot of tips that she saves in a jar to send to Shirley. She also writes letters telling Shirley about her life and work in Los Angeles. In them, she reminds her daughter to study and get good grades. Soon, she tells her, she will have enough money to get her own place and bring her to LA.

By spring, Copply is ready to keep that promise. After spending a year living in her father's world, Shirley is anxious to join her mother. When school is out, she hugs Carl Henry goodbye, boards a Greyhound bus, and heads west for that reunion. She smiles a satisfied smile as she reclines her seat and drifts off to sleep.

Copply remembers her friends back in Safford—most are still there. One day after work, she asks Ozella for a pen and some paper. She sits down at the kitchen table and writes a letter to her good friend Pearlie Mae.

Dear Pearl,

How are you and the kids? Fine, I hope. I am writing to let you know that I'm in California. Yes, I finally made it all the way here! I wish I could tell you everything that has happened since we were last together, but it would take way too long. I'm just glad that I've made it through a lot and am now in the place where I want to be. The kids are still in Arizona but not for long. Shirley is in high school—can you believe it? Junior has dropped out of school and is talking about going into the service.

Girl, I'm working as a waitress in a big store. Yes—me, a waitress! Pearl, I make more money every day than I made in a week in Safford. I guess you can say I'm pickin' in high cotton! I'm staying with my cousin for now, but I hope to have a place of my own soon. That's when Shirley will come here to finish school. I miss her.

Please say hello to all the girls. I miss all of you but especially you, Pearlie. I hope you're taking care of yourself. Remember, you'll always have me for a friend.

Goodbye for now. I'll close this letter but never my heart.

Love,
Copply

After two months of earning a modest salary and many tips, Copply is able to move into a small bachelor's apartment in back of Ruby and Wilson Dupree's residence on South

Gramercy Place. It's near her job and in a nice, racially integrated neighborhood on Los Angeles's coveted west side. It's
tight but adequate for now.

By the time Shirley arrives, her mother has also found a
new love, Johnny Faulk, a man she knew as a child back in
Texas. His family lived on the neighboring farm. He is a recent
divorcée who knows Ozella, who was instrumental in recon-
necting them. He is a longtime admirer of Copply. They begin
courting. He proposes, and in the next year, he becomes her
third husband.

Summer in LA is mind-bogglingly different for Shirley.
She enrolls in summer school at one of the city's prestigious
high schools, where she meets many new friends who invite
her to parties and introduce her to the beach. She thorough-
ly enjoys the freedom of the life teens live in this place—so
much to do and few restrictions. But there's this new man in
Copply's life, and space is limited. Her discomfort causes her
to decide to return to Tucson for the next school year.

This time, she will live with the other grandmother,
Earlee—Copply's biological mother—and her husband,
Charlie Jackson, who have moved to Tucson from Texas and
built a home on South Park Avenue, near where the family
started. Although she loves her father and the many ways he
spoils her—money, clothes, car—his home life is too chaotic
for Shirley. Many strangers in and out and no boundaries for
her social activities. This feels too unsafe for one who has been

raised with lots of discipline and structure. Her grandparents' will be a safe place. She will have freedom within limits. At least there will be church every Sunday. This works for everyone. Earlee is a proud woman who is quiet, creative, and ambitious. She will be a good influence on Shirley.

Copply and Johnny marry and purchase a duplex down the street from the apartment. Earlee and Charlie enjoy having the company of a grandchild, most of the time, and Shirley gets a chance to continue her education in a familiar setting, where she achieves many honors. Copply stays on at Von's. Johnny works at the naval station in San Pedro. The couple is happy and enjoy friends in their new home.

After one more year there, Shirley decides to leave Arizona and move permanently to Los Angeles. She enrolls in Manual Arts High School as a senior. Copply is content to have her under her roof again. She helps her get hired part-time at the snack bar. Her head spins as Shirley gets involved in myriad social activities and carries a full academic load at school.

Amid her delight at the adjustment her daughter makes to the new life, she watches the people, especially the boys, who are introduced. Her fondest hope is that Shirley will exceed her own life's status; that she will go to college, get a degree, and "be somebody." Guiding her to and through that aspiration will become her greatest challenge. She decides to set the bar high.

"I don't want you to get boy-struck," she tells Shirley as

they wash dishes together. "There's more to life than boys and babies. I want you to go to college and get a degree so you won't have to work as hard as I have. I want you to make something of yourself. Use that smart head of yours for more than a hat rack."

They both laugh at this joke. Shirley gets the message loud and clear.

The next year, Copply leaves Von's to work as a cook for residents of a fraternity house on the campus of the University of Southern California. It is easy work; the boys are not picky eaters. They just want a lot of whatever she prepares. She often brings leftover food home for dinner.

Something about the college campus is infectious to Copply. She enjoys being around books and the banter of youthful students. It inspires a desire in her to be more than a cook—to "*be somebody*" herself.

"Have you ever thought about real estate?" one of the fraternity residents asks her during a casual conversation.

"Real estate?" Copply isn't sure she knows what he is talking about.

"Yeah, people make a lot of money selling houses out here. You should think about it." He grabs a cookie and rushes out the door.

Copply is gob-smacked by the frat student's words. Her interest is raised astronomically by the thought of making a lot of money. She notices many real estate offices along her route home. She decides that one day she will stop into one of them to find out more and to learn how to get into the business.

When she does this, she finds out that practicing real estate listing and selling requires a license. She's given information about real estate schools where she can learn all about the business, and if she's successful at passing a test, she can become a licensed salesperson.

When Shirley graduates from Manual Arts High School and starts attending junior college, Copply enrolls in real estate school, passes the test, and becomes a salesperson. She applies to several real estate offices. She is turned down at some of them but is finally accepted into a west-side office that covers a residential territory near her home.

It is a territory into which many Black people are beginning to move, a kind of migration from segregated older neighborhoods of south and east LA to more prestigious hillside neighborhoods once populated by wealthy white people that feature large stucco homes with tile roofs.

Copply dives headlong into her new work, dressing up every day, getting her hair done by professional hairdressers, and wearing full makeup. Hers is a complete makeover. She meets new, interesting people among her clients. She charms them with her bright smile and quick wit—accessories of her salesmanship.

She spends many long hours in the field, only these "fields" are not cotton fields—they are lined with cash. She's as happy as a hog in slop! Never did she ever imagine she could live like this! If only Johnny would show some enthusiasm. She needs his support.

"When are you coming to bed?" This is his most frequently asked question—never one about her work.

He is disenchanted with this change—too much change for him. He misses their evening television time together. Now he spends many late evenings watching Roller Derby alone while Copply closes real estate deals.

Within the first five years that Copply is a Realtor, she sells many of the homes in Ladera Heights, Windsor Hills, and View Park. She has found her niche. She is tempted many times to buy one of the luxury homes for herself but backs away when Johnny displays profound disinterest. By now, he is retired from his job and seems content to live a laid-back life-style. But she's on fire and has no intention of slowing down.

With Shirley now about to graduate from UCLA, where she has transferred after meeting the two-year residency requirement, her life is just taking off. She will have an empty nest, and she's anxious to see the world.

She studies for and achieves a real estate broker's license. She is definitely driving her own destiny. With this license, she owns her own business and begins to create some serious wealth. As a sole proprietor, she does not have to split her commissions; it's all hers.

She gets a call from her best friend, Annie. "Hey there, Cope. I haven't heard from you in too long. I know you're in real estate now. You must be busy. Folks are buying up all the vacant property around here. I hope you're getting in on it. How is Johnny enjoying all of this?"

Copply closes the kitchen door and speaks in a low voice. "Hey, Annie, it's great to hear your voice. I sure miss you and the girls at the snack bar. We'll have to get together one day soon. Listen, I'm loving my work. The money is better than I ever dreamed, but Johnny and I aren't doing so well. He doesn't want to go anyplace or do anything. He just sits on the front porch and rocks in the rocking chair all day. He is such a bore. I have no place to spend this money. If he doesn't change soon, he'll have to go. I can't let him drag me backward. I'll keep you posted."

Annie expresses her disappointment and sadness in hearing this news. The couple is dissolving after twenty-five years of marriage. She hangs up the phone thinking, *What a shame!*

After graduation from college, Shirley is hired to teach in one of LA's most prestigious elementary schools, located in the hills of Bel Air. Copply is very proud. She has seen her daughter through many rough patches on the road to this success. They've worked it out together. Shirley has become *"somebody"* by her definition. Now she's watching closely the parade of people who drift in and out of the house—especially the male suitors who are introduced. They are a mixed bag, an assortment of would-be movie stars, musicians, and athletic jocks. She scrutinizes and criticizes each one, hoping to help her daughter avoid the missteps and heartache that she endured.

"She drags in some of the strangest characters," Copply tells her best friend, Annie.

Eventually, Shirley starts dating a young man who meets with Copply's approval. He's a UCLA math graduate, and he knows how to play her favorite games, Bid-Whist and dominoes. He and Copply are always partners when he comes over and a game starts. They enjoy winning—beating all competitors. Shirley is never invited to play. She can't play with the proficiency of the two kingpins. Counting cards is not what she does well. To save face, she doesn't even try.

"Come on, you're taking too long. It'll be Christmas pretty soon!"

Copply's bark is embarrassing to Shirley. No one defends her, not even her boyfriend. To avoid feeling ostracized, she busies herself with checking students' papers or talking to girlfriends on the phone in a back room. She closes the door to the back room to block the sound of hoots, "wuffin'," and the loud sounds of playing cards and dominoes slapping on the dining room table.

"Come on, play that ace. I know you got it!"

"All right, partner, let's show these rookies what a 'Boston' looks like!" *Slam!*

"Give me five—no, make that ten. Ooo-we-eee!"

Shirley forfeits date time with this boyfriend for *this*. They don't go out for dinners or to attend movies, dances, or plays. He's her mother's choice for her future husband. Clearly, he's in first place in the lineup.

After a year of the courtship, Shirley and Kenneth Brandon are married in a small church wedding attended by family, friends, and a host of young children who are Shirley's students. The wedding party is sparse: there is only one attendant for Shirley, a maid of honor, a best man for Kenneth, a flower girl, and a ring bearer. Carl Henry comes from Tucson to walk his daughter down the aisle and give her away. His chest nearly bursts with pride when he sees her dressed in her beautiful lace wedding gown. He can't stop looking at her.

When school is out for summer break, Shirley and her husband leave Los Angeles. His new job with a computer company transfers him to an air base in New Jersey to work on a government contract. Shirley is sad to leave her teaching position, where she is making her mark as the first Black teacher. Her impact at that school would become storied.

They stay on the East Coast for nearly three years before returning to Los Angeles, bringing with them a two-year-old son. He is the first of three children the couple have during their fifteen-year marriage.

Copply delights in the grandchildren, spending birthday and holiday time as well as frequent home visits. She's always there to help Shirley after births. She dyes Easter eggs with the children and hides them for the hunt.

When trouble brews in Shirley and Kenneth's marriage, Copply tries hard to help the young couple stay together. She could offer money, but money wasn't the problem—it was beyond her reach. Her heart is broken when the marriage ends. He would always be her son-in-law.

One year after Shirley's divorce from Kenneth, she remarries, this time to a man she met while working in city hall, Ernest Sprinkles. He is a public figure in the city— well-known by many. The large fairytale wedding, attended by a substantial number of LA's Black elite, is the culmination of a whirlwind romance.

They buy the home of Shirley's dreams in a hilly Culver City subdivision and strike out on a fantasy lifestyle, blending two families into one. The romance is topped a year later by the birth of a son, whom they adore.

Copply is tolerant but never fully accepts the mate Shirley chooses for her second marriage. He never plays cards or goes fishing with her and Johnny as Kenneth had done.

Together, Shirley and Ernie parent a blended family of six children. Everything seems frothy and wonder-filled for the first five years. Then things begin to unravel: obstinate, uncooperative teenagers; ambitious, ill-advised business decisions made by Ernie; serious debt and other problems that threaten their secure base.

By the eighth year, the marriage is headed for divorce court. Ernie, wounded deeply by a sense of failure, moves away, leaving Shirley with mortgage debts that force her under water. She needs a financial bailout, but Copply is unwilling to contribute. She is forced to find refuge in the upstairs duplex apartment above her mother. Yes, she is back in Copply's house. This is the last place she wants to live! She and her children must now regroup. The rent is well within her budget—$225 a month, to be paid on time.

At some point prior to Shirley's return, after twenty-five years, the marriage of Copply and Johnny fails the stress test too. They divorce and go their separate ways. She remains in the house on Gramercy, and he moves into one side of a rental duplex that they own and that he gets in the divorce settlement. Shirley and the kids are distressed by these events. Johnny is the only grandpa the children know. They call him Paw-Paw. After the divorce, they never see him again—for years. When he dies, Shirley attends his services with his three adult children from his first marriage and Copply. All of the grandchildren, now grown, live far, far away.

Shirley refuses to be defeated—set back, yes; defeated, no! She is determined to right her ship. She stays in Copply's upstairs apartment for eight years. She returns to teaching, attends night classes, earns a master's degree, is promoted, and works in two well-paying administrative positions.

Next, she purchases another home in a town ninety miles east of LA. She lives and works there for one year until she is lured to Texas by the prospect of a full scholarship to a prestigious PhD program at Texas's flagship university, UT Austin, and by the invitation of an old male Tucson admirer, also divorced, who lives there. Against all odds, Shirley picks up and moves to Texas—the place where her life began.

Copply is, once again, very skeptical of Shirley's moves, but she doesn't express cynicism. She is kept informed of Shirley's progress in frequent phone calls. After one year of trying, the relationship that lured her to Texas falls apart, and Shirley moves into her own space and moves on. She will not be derailed. Shirley senses her mother's loneliness and that she's drinking more than she should. She sometimes hears this in Copply's slurred words. Shirley is worried about her mom and asks Annie to look in on her. She can trust her to do this.

Shirley puts her head down and works hard to earn the degree that will place her at the top of her profession and make Copply proud. She's determined.

PART
4

"What you are to be, you are now becoming."
(Carl Rogers)

Victory

Children, I come back today
To tell you a story of the long dark way
That I had to climb, that I had to know
In order that our race might live and grow.
Three hundred years in the deepest South:
But God put a dream and a song in my mouth.
God put a dream like steel in my soul.
Now, through my children, I'm reaching my goal.
Now, through my children, young and free,
I realize the blessings denied to me . . .
I nourished the dream that nothing could smother
Deep in my breast, the Negro Mother.

By Langston Hughes

When the time finally arrives for Shirley's graduation, Copply anxiously boards a plane to see her and to attend the Texas ceremony. She can't believe that Shirley loves it there and plans to stay. She, whose birthplace was a small east Texas town that became renowned for a very controversial public greeting: "Welcome to Greenville, the *blackest land* and the *whitest people!*"

Texas was a place that, as a young woman, Copply couldn't wait to *leave*. She left many years ago and only returned a few times to visit or bury family members. She never considered living in Texas again. She is perplexed at Shirley's decision.

Relatives and friends begin pouring in from all over the country, finding seats to observe the granting of Shirley's doctorate degree. All of her four children and two grandchildren are among those who watch and applaud loudly when her name is called and Shirley marches across the massive stage of UT's Performing Arts Center to receive her diploma. There are hoots and celebratory whistles from Shirley's classmates who have come to know and appreciate her; she traveled with them to Europe, taking in Paris, Belgium, Germany, and Holland. She argued against and with them in numerous classroom educational policy debates, enlightening them on the history and pejorative, demeaning nature of Jim Crow laws and school segregation—pointing out that vestiges of it are still observable. Shirley is older than they are, as she is graduating at fifty-five years old, and her life experiences are vast compared with theirs. Arizona, California, and New Jersey have been her training grounds. And not one of them has ever lived or worked in a cotton patch. They cannot know what she knows. Her different perspectives are not always received kindly. Nevertheless, she persists in sharing her often unorthodox beliefs that pertain to effective, equitable teaching of all children.

For Copply, this auspicious occasion is like popping the cork on a bottle of the world's best wine—she cannot possibly feel more satisfaction and pride. It is a day long in coming, when one of her children takes the long walk to the edge of the proverbial diving board, fully ready to swim toward all of life's rewards. After risking and surviving many hard knocks and pitfalls, Shirley is on her way to the better life that she deserves. She has gotten up each time she was knocked down, determined to get to that better place. She is still relatively young. There's lots more life to be lived.

When graduation is over, Copply spots Shirley outside in the crowd. She rushes over to meet her. The two women grab each other, embrace, kiss, and repeatedly squeeze each other tightly. Copply pushes Shirley back to look her squarely in the eyes. No words are exchanged—the tearful smiles say it all. Copply's heart is full of joy. She scans the huge midyear graduating class. Although the brick-lined apron of the auditorium is crowded with happy graduates, Shirley is the only Black one she sees wearing the cape of a PhD.

Her dream has come full circle. With property investments, a substantial bank account, good health, and now a daughter who has scaled the wall to her highest academic degree, every wish is fulfilled. She takes a seat on a nearby park bench, watching while friends and family surround Shirley with hugs, flowers, and praise. There is a cacophony of laughter and chatter.

Her mind turns to Pearlie and Roger, both of whom are now dead and buried. Both died of tuberculosis. She looks toward the clear blue sky. She smiles. She imagines that she's standing between their tombstones, touching them lightly with her hands. She can barely hold back the tears of joy and a strong urge to shout out loud, "Look, Daddy! Look, Pearlie! I hope you can see us down here now. It took a long time getting to this field, but here we are. We're sho' 'nuff *pickin' in high cotton!*"

Giving my mother a kiss at my college graduation.

Acknowledgments

I owe a debt of gratitude to so many who encouraged me as I wrote this story. From some, it was words of encouragement, "Atta girls," that kept me going: James Cohen, Ernie McCray, Mildred West, Bob Farrell, Joanna Landcaster, and Joan Riley are among this group. Others were more intimately involved in the reading, re-reading, advising, and critiquing as I doggedly trudged onward to the end: Vicky Westmore, Victoria Luca, and my diligent student assistant, Maia Helvy can be credited with this more intense level of involvement. Because of them, a screenplay, *High Cotton*, was spun from the substance of the first chapter.

Thanks, also, to the exceptional publishing guidance of the Wheatmark team; especially to Mark Dupaul and Lori Conser, without whose patience and expertise this book would not have seen the light of day. Publishing a book is a lot like birthing a baby—personal and painful. I've been gently led through the process by these kind, competent people.

For my family, I hope this book will be a source of historical knowledge and inspiration: proof that, "All things are possible to the courageous"*—and, to the "intentional."

*Marian Anderson

About the Author

Shirley Robinson Sprinkles was born in Greenville, Texas. Her parents, Copply and Carl Henry Robinson, welcomed her into the family as their second child when their son, Carl Junior, was two months from his second birthday. Life in the small East Texas town was hard for the young couple, who barely eked out a living picking cotton. Their home had a leaky roof, out-door running water, and a "out-house" toilet. Jim Crow laws kept them suspended on the bottom rung of society—poor and deprived of opportunity to advance.

These intolerable conditions motivated the couple's move westward toward California, rumored to be a "Mecca" for Black people. With limited funds to go the distance from Texas to

California, the family, of necessity, stopped in Safford Arizona to work in cotton fields in hopes of earning enough money to one day carry out their plan. This place is the first that Shirley remembers. It was where she learned to talk and play with a caregiver's children while her parents worked.

In time, the family unit dissolved, and Shirley accompanied her mother on a long, complex journey through life in Tucson, where she grew up, thrived, and achieved academically and socially. When her mother abruptly left Tucson to find a better life in California, Shirley lived there for two more years in the care of her father and her grandparents. She eventually joined her mother in Los Angeles where she finished high school and college. She chose teaching as a career and pursued many paths in the education field throughout her life, including earning a PhD in educational leadership at UT/ Austin. It had been a long, long, journey from cotton patch poverty to the richness of life; financial success, and the esteem of colleagues and scholars.

Today, Shirley Robinson Sprinkles still lives in Austin, Texas. In addition to writing books and essays, she continues to contribute to schools and students through School Board service. She is a devoted mother, grandmother, and wife.

When people ask her, "What's next?" Shirley's favorite answer is, "*I'm gonna keep picking 'til I get to the end of my row!*"

Books published by this author are:

From Dunbar to Destiny: One Woman's Journey Through Desegregation and Beyond

Seven Essential Keys to Successful Single Parenting

Platitudes and Attitudes

Grandma's Special Visit

Bill's Balloon

Implementing a Complex Classroom Innovation: Process, Problems and Potential (Dissertation)